KEY SKILLS IN ENGLISH

Janna Tiearney

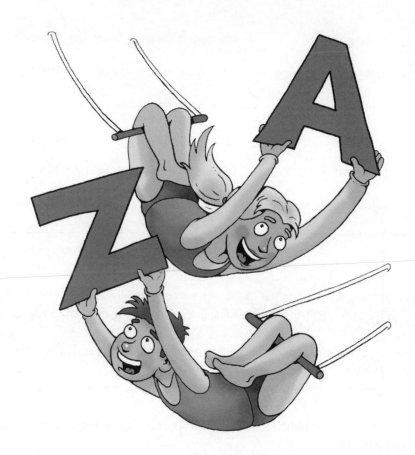

Third Class

Activity Book

g GILL EDUCATION

Introduction to Teachers and Parents

This book is one of a series of English Skills Books aimed at children in First to Sixth Class: 1, 2, 3, 4, 5 and 6. The *Lift Off!* series has been written by an experienced primary school teacher, Janna Tiearney who has devised a specific scheme of work on the teaching of core English skills in direct response to feedback from teachers around the country.

How to use this book

This book is self-contained and designed to be used independently by children alongside any core English programme. This book is laid out in a child-friendly manner and includes contemporary and engaging artwork and themes. The reading texts and exercises have been carefully graded and each book is a continuation and revision of the content of the previous book. The earlier books naturally place a greater emphasis on word sounds and phonics, while the later books focus more on grammar. All books contain a consistent format of activities to promote children's confidence. Each unit covers all three strands of the English curriculum: reading, writing and oral language. Each unit, in each book, consists of 6 pages. Each page carries its own *Friendly Owl* icon in the top corner of the page.

Page	Icon		Content
Page 1		Reading	Pre-reading question, illustration and reading text
Page 2		Reading & responding	'Talk about' topic, comprehension and higher order questions
Page 3		Sounds	Letter sounds and phonics activities using visual support
Page 4		Grammar	Activities including rules, examples, drill and practice questions
Page 5		Looking at words	Spelling activities using sight words from the reading section
Page 6		Extra optional page	Optional drama, personal writing and a fun puzzle section

Other features

- **'Before you read ...'** question: will capture the child's interest and give him/her a purpose for reading.
- **'Talk about'** oral language activities follow each reading piece encouraging children to engage fully with the text and create their own meaning.
- **Information bubbles** are dotted throughout the book for the purpose of fun, as points of information and to promote further thinking on the theme or given concept.
- **'Remember boxes'** are used throughout the grammar sections to assess and remind children of what they have learned already.
- **'Sample boxes'** provide the children with important, accessible examples to ensure they understand the grammar point before completing the task.
- **Revision pages** appear at key stages in the book to promote the revisiting and consolidation of letter sounds and crucial grammar points and as a means of assessing progress during the year.
- **Integrated activities within each unit:** The personal writing, sight words, and oral language activities are linked to the reading text. This means that the children are familiar with the topic by the time they come to write about it.
- **Comprehensive sight word list:** Each unit has a list of sight words that children can read in context. By completing the sight word activities in each unit, children are able to build up a comprehensive list of sight words, which they can then use in their own writing and reading.
- **Effective spelling strategies:** The 'Looking at words' page uses the *Look and say, picture, cover, write and check* method to teach spellings. A word list is provided and there are spaces to record the spellings and more spaces to correct any spelling mistakes. Other word recognition strategies have been included to encourage children to find the strategies that work best for them.

Third Class Activity Book
Contents

Has anyone been kind to you lately?

1.   Read the story.

An African tale – How the cheetah got his speed

Once upon a time, the Creator wanted to find out which of his animals was the fastest. He gathered the animals together.

'We will have a race,' said the Creator. He chose the cheetah and the fastest of all antelopes.

Back then, the cheetah had soft paws, so he had to borrow a set of paws from the wild dog.

The race started from a tree and was to end at a hill in the distance. The Creator was looking on as the race began. The animals lined up. The wild dog said, 'On your marks, get set, go!'

The animals were off. Soon the antelope was way ahead. He was sure to win. Then suddenly he stumbled on a stone and fell. He had hurt his leg and could not get up.

The cheetah reached the antelope. Instead of running ahead to win, he stopped next to the injured antelope.

'I will help you up,' said the kind cheetah.

The Creator was happy to see this act of kindness.

'I will give you a gift, cheetah,' he said. 'You will be the fastest animal in the land and you can keep the paws of the wild dog.'

This is how the cheetah comes to be the fastest animal. It can reach speeds of 100 kilometres per hour!

A cheetah cannot pull in its claws like other cats.

2. Talk about.
Talk about different acts of kindness you have seen.
How can we show kindness to others?

3. Answer the questions.

Remember Write full sentences.

a.   Who was chosen for the race?

_____

b.   What did the cheetah borrow?

_____

c.   Where did the race start?

_____

d.   Who was the race starter?

_____

e.   What happened to the antelope?

_____

f.   What gift did the cheetah receive?

_____

4. Write the answers.
a.   What kind of character do you think the cheetah had?

_____

b.   Why did the cheetah receive a gift?

_____

c.   Is a cheetah faster than you on your bicycle? Explain your answer.

_____

d.   Name one way in which you can show kindness to others.

_____

5. Find words in the story with the same meaning.
a.   collected together   _____
b.   tripped   _____
c.   hurt   _____
d.   animal feet   _____
e.   60 minutes   _____

6. Write the blends to complete the words. Read the sentences.

sw	sp	st	sk	sl	sc

a. A__ __ the __ __eet teacher for a __ __one.

b. __ __ars __ __arkle in the __ __y.

c. Do not __ __ip on the wet __ __reet.

d. __ __op __ __eeping in class.

e. Sit __ __ill on the naughty __ __ep.

> Always try your best at school.

7. Circle the correct words. Write the sentences.

a. Wear your (mask / mast) to the Hallowe'en party.

_____

b. Put your money in the (band / bank).

_____

c. Please (lend / left) me your (lend / left) shoe.

_____

d. You can (truck / trust) me with your (truck / trust).

_____

e. (Check / Chest) to see if there is gold in the (check / chest).

_____

> I lost my lock in the nest.

8. Make words. Circle the nonsense words.

Add **st**.	Add **sk**.	Add **mp**.	Add **ck**.
ru__ __	ru__ __	ru__ __	ru__ __
li__ __	li__ __	li__ __	li__ __
lo__ __	lo__ __	lo__ __	lo__ __
ne__ __	ne__ __	ne__ __	ne__ __

9. Write a silly sentence using words with blends.

_____

_____

_____

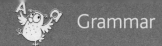
Capital letters are used at the beginning of a sentence and for names, titles, places, days of the week, months of the year, special days and for I.
Full stops are used at the end of a sentence.
Question marks are used at the end of a question.

10. Write the words that need capital letters.

    a.   sea, beach, spain, holiday _____

    b.   girl, little, school, ann _____

    c.   you, i, them, we _____

    d.   friday, weekend, day, week _____

    e.   month, year, june, break _____

    f.   gifts, snow, turkey, christmas _____

> In Dublin's fair city, where the .....

11. Write the sentences correctly.

    Remember Punctuation marks.

    a.   my friend and i are going to dublin

    _____

    b.   every tuesday i clean my room

    _____

    c.   this easter miss green will buy us eggs

    _____

    d.   when will you finish this work

    _____

    e.   greg and susan want to visit london in august

    _____

    f.   the winter months are november december and january

    _____

12. Use these words to make sentences of your own.

    a.   books   _____

    b.   why   _____

    c.   rain   _____

    d.   write   _____

    e.   talk   _____

Word list

| which | hurt | got | upon | together | end | time | way |

13. Learn the spellings. Now look and say, picture, cover, write, check.

_____   _____

_____   _____

_____   _____

_____   _____

14. Write any words you got wrong.

_____

15. Write the missing words. Use the word list.

    a.   Pam doesn't know _____ puppy to choose.

    b.   Once _____ a time, there was a great Third Class.

    c.   It is almost _____ to go home.

    d.   Take a map so you don't lose your _____ .

16. Use these words to make sentences of your own.

    a.   hurt   _____

    b.   got   _____

    c.   together   _____

    d.   end   _____

When will this work **end**?

17. Write the answers. Use the word list.

    Syllables are the number of claps in a word.

    | **Example** mon + key = monkey |

    a.   Find smaller words in **got** and **time**. _____

    b.   Break **upon** into smaller words. _____ _____

    c.   Break **together** into smaller words. _____ _____ _____

    d.   Write three words that include the letter **h**.

          _____ _____ _____

    e.   Clap the list words. How many words have one syllable? _____

    f.   Change one letter in each word to make words from the list:

          why _____   **get** _____   **tide** _____

Drama

18. Work with a group to act out the story of
    How the cheetah got its speed.

    Read Aesop's Fables at www.aesopfables.com
    Show kindness to each other for the rest of the day!

Write about

19. Write a short story about how an animal got a special
    feature, for instance, how the rhino got its horn, how the
    cat got its whiskers or how the elephant got its trunk.
    Make a rough plan for your story below.

20. Write out your story neatly. Read and check it.
    Draw a picture to go with it. Display it in the classroom.

21. Match the animals to their footprints.

A hedgehog has four clawed toes.
A hippo has four toes.
A zebra footprint looks like a horse footprint with a single large toe.
A lion has padded toes. Its claws are fully sheathed.
A white rhino has three toes.
The elephant's front feet are oval with five toes.

A cheetah will not usually harm humans.

Before you read... Have you been away on holiday?
1. Read the postcard.

Dear James,

Having a super time in Spain. Weather is hot, pools are cold! Having great craic on the beach. I have tried surfing.

I am not enjoying the food! I am missing sausages and mash! Yesterday we went to a theme park. The rides were exciting, but my sister got sick. We're going to a water park tomorrow.

Well, that's all for now. See you in about a week.

From Paddy

James Reilly

6 River Heights

Ballywater

Co. Cavan

Ireland

A change is as good as a holiday.

He that travels far knows much.

2. Talk about.

Do you enjoy the hot weather? Talk about how activities might be different in hot and cold countries. Have a class vote to find out the most popular place for a holiday.

3. Answer the questions.

> **Remember** Write full sentences.

a. Who wrote the postcard?

_____

b. Where is he?

_____

c. What part of the holiday is he not enjoying?

_____

d. Which water sport did he try?

_____

e. Where were they going the next day?

_____

f. In which county does his friend live?

_____

4. Write the answers.

a. Do you think Paddy was enjoying the holiday? Explain your answer.

_____

b. What kinds of food might he be eating?

_____

c. Name a ride he might find at the theme park.

_____

d. What season do you think it is? Explain your answer.

_____

5. Answer **yes**, **no** or **maybe**.

a. The postcard was sent from Spain to Ireland. _____

b. Paddy's sister was on a rollercoaster. _____

c. The water in the pools was warm. _____

d. Paddy spent two weeks in Spain. _____

e. They were having fun on the beach. _____

f. Paddy does not like sausages. _____

Sometimes two letters make one sound.

> **Sample** **ea** in b**ea**t

6. Write the missing **a** sounds. (All the words will have an **a** sound as in **way**.)

> eigh   ay   ai   ei   ea   ey

   a.   Please bring me st___ ___k on a tr___ ___.
   b.   Th___ ___ had a gr___ ___t day.
   c.   You should p___ ___ me ___ ___ ___ ___t euro.
   d.   The r___ ___ndeer could not pull the sl___ ___ ___ ___.
   e.   You can pl___ ___ with my tr___ ___n if you don't br___ ___k it.

7. Write the missing **e** sounds. (All the words will have an **e** sound as in **see**.)

> ee   ea   ey   ie

Hey, Santa, this **sleigh weighs** a ton.

   a.   A b___ ___ gives us hon___ ___.
   b.   An ___ ___l makes a delicious m___ ___l.
   c.   You should r___ ___d before you sl___ ___p.
   d.   I cannot s___ ___ the monk___ ___
       in the tr___ ___.
   e.   The football t___ ___m is on the f___ ___ld.

8. Sort the words by their letter sounds. Add your own word to each column.

> meat   steak   leaf   great   sea   beak

ea as in **break**	ea as in **wheat**

The rain in Spain falls mainly on the plain.

9. Write the sentences correctly. (There are two sentences on each line).

    a.   my cat's name is jessie she is black

        _____

    b.   i want to visit africa it is a hot country

        _____

    c.   in december it is cold i like the snow

        _____

    d.   my friend is called mary we love to chat

        _____

    e.   we break up on friday i will miss school

        _____

10. You are the teacher! Use a red pen to correct the sentences.

    a.   my father's name is mr. mouse
    b.   the class is going to belfast in july
    c.   my dog rex has eaten my slippers
    d.   why is tom jumping up and down
    e.   who has been to mayo
    f.   the teacher is taking a holiday in australia
    g.   where is joe going
    h.   how does matthew get to school

Remember Names begin with a capital letter.
Sentences end with a full stop.

11. Complete the sentences using your own words.

    a.   My pet's name is _____
    b.   I live in _____
    c.   The principal's name is _____
    d.   I have a cousin called _____
    e.   I know a boy called _____
    f.   There is an actor called _____
    g.   My neighbour's name is _____
    h.   If I had a pet rhino, I would call it _____
    i.   The president's name is _____
    j.   My surname is _____

Word list

| great | beach | sister | about | week | dear | rides | water |

12. Learn the spellings. Now look and say, picture, cover, write, check.

_____   _____

_____   _____

_____   _____

_____   _____

13. Write any words you got wrong.

_____

14. Write the missing words. Use the word list.

    a.   In Science we are learning _____ insects.

    b.   Seven days is one _____ .

    c.   My _____ and I do not get along.

    d.   Please _____ those thirsty plants.

15. In your copybook use these words to make sentences of your own: **great**, **beach**, **dear** and **rides**.

I am having a **great** day.

16. Write the answers. Use the word list.

    a.   Find smaller words in:

        water _____   **sister** _____

        great _____   **dear** _____

        beach _____

    b.   Write words from the list that have two syllables.

        _____

    c.   Find three words with the **ea** letter pattern.

        _____

    d.   Do they all sound the same? _____

    e.   If the words were in alphabetical order, write the word that would be last. _____

    f.   Change one letter in each of these words to make words from the list.

        weak _____   **bench** _____

        pear _____   **greet** _____

Drama

17. Work with a group. Act out a holiday scene. Make sure everyone has an acting role.

18. Recite the poem.

WISH YOU WERE HERE
Dear All,
The sea looks great, but I've not tested –
Locals say it's shark-infested.
Beach looks fine, I'm not complaining –
Go there, soon as it stops raining.
The food's okay, if you like fish –
And things that crawl across your dish.
As for our hotel, it's neat –
It should be great when it's complete.
I'll bring you back a souvenir –
Goodbye for now, wish you were here.
(And I wasn't)

Colin McNaughton

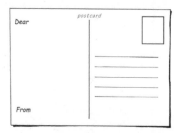

Write about

19. Imagine you are on holiday. In your copybook, write a postcard to a friend.

> The top holiday destinations are
> France, the USA and Spain.

20. Match the airport codes to the destinations.

BER	Calcutta, India
DUB	Shannon
GWY	Buffalo, New York, USA
CPT	Dublin
JFK	Sydney, Australia
BCN	Berlin, Germany
SNN	Cape Town, South Africa
CDG	Paris, France, Charles de Gaulle
BUF	Galway
CCU	New York, USA, John F. Kennedy
SYD	Cairo, Egypt
CAI	Barcelona, Spain

What meals would you like to see on a menu?
1. Read the menu.

Gruesome Grill

Set menu

Starters

Fried toad legs with melted cheese,
Or spider heads and mushy peas,
Or steamed fingers served with rice,
Or plump and juicy boiled mice.

Main courses

Slimy fish eyes soaked in milk,
Or roasted silkworms and their silk,
Or grilled grasshoppers, fresh and hot,
Or slug stew served up in a pot.

All of these come with rotten chips,
And a variety of snotty dips.

Desserts

Bones in jelly with lizard cake,
Or chopped-up liver and snail milkshake.

Stinky cheese all green and blue.
Worm-filled chocolates you can chew.
€35.00 per person.

Bon appetit!

Rattlesnakes are eaten in Texas, U.S.A.

Fried spiders are on the menu in Thailand.

2. Talk about.

    Is there anything edible on the menu? Talk about your favourite meals.

3. Answer the questions.

    Remember Write full sentences.

    a. Which vegetable is served with spiders?

    _____

    b. Which dish is served in a pot?

    _____

    c. How many desserts are there?

    _____

    d. What is served with rice?

    _____

    e. Name four different cooking methods.

    _____

    f. What would a meal for two cost?

    _____

4. Write the answers.

    a. Is there anything on the menu you would eat? Explain your answer.

    _____

    b. What does **Bon appetit** mean?

    _____

    c. Give the restaurant another name.

    _____

    d. Write another dish for this menu.

    _____

5. Draw a picture of one of these meals.

    Spider heads and mushy peas.
    Slimy fish eyes soaked in milk.
    Bones in jelly with lizard cake.
    Worm-filled chocolates.

6. Write the missing **i** sounds. (All the words will have an **i** sound as in **pie**.)

> **igh   ie**

a. Your t___ ___ is very br___ ___ ___t.
b. Last n___ ___ ___t I had a chicken p___ ___.
c. Do not f___ ___ ___t with a kn___ ___ ___t.
d. To l___ ___ is not r___ ___ ___t.
e. Without l___ ___ ___t the plant will d___ ___.

7. Write your own sentence using words with these sounds.

_____

8. Write the missing **o** sounds. (All the words will have an **o** sound as in **snow**.)

> **ow   oa   oe**

a. There is a g___ ___t at your wind___ ___.
b. Do not thr___ ___ sn___ ___ on my t___ ___.
c. A t___ ___d is not yell___ ___.
d. Our t___ ___ster is so sl___ ___.
e. Let me sh___ ___ you my b___ ___t.

9. Write your own sentence using words with these sounds.

_____

10. Write the missing **u** sounds. (All the words will have an **u** sound as in **new**.)

> **ew   ue**

a. A f___ ___ boys will arg___ ___.
b. I need a n___ ___ tiss___ ___.
c. Jack kn___ ___ they would resc___ ___ him.
d. St___ ___ is good val___ ___.
e. It's a good vi___ ___ from the stat___ ___.

11. Write your own sentence using words with these sounds.

_____

Plurals mean more than one. Sometimes we add **'s'** to form plurals. If the word ends in a hissing sound, such as **x**, **sh**, **ch**, **s**, we add **es**.

> **Sample** desk – desks, latch – latches

12. Write the words as plurals.

a.	bed	_____	f.	chair	_____
b.	watch	_____	g.	kid	_____
c.	kiss	_____	h.	bush	_____
d.	rash	_____	i.	plant	_____
e.	fox	_____	j.	tree	_____

If the word ends in a **y** and the letter that comes before the **y** is a consonant, then change **y** to **i** and add **es**. If the letter before the **y** is a vowel, then just add **s**.

I am reading stor**ies** to the cats.

> **Sample** nappy – nappies, storey – storeys

13. Write the words as plurals.

a.	fairy	_____	f.	puppy	_____
b.	daisy	_____	g.	fly	_____
c.	chimney	_____	h.	valley	_____
d.	toy	_____	i.	baby	_____
e.	berry	_____	j.	lady	_____

If the word ends in an **f** add **ves**. If the word ends in **ff** just add **s**.

> **Sample** cuff – cuffs, sheaf – sheaves

14. Write the words as plurals.

> **Tricky ones** roof – roofs, reef – reefs, chief – chiefs, dwarf can be dwarfs or dwarves.

a.	loaf	_____	f.	scarf	_____
b.	shelf	_____	g.	life	_____
c.	leaf	_____	h.	thief	_____
d.	knife	_____	i.	wife	_____
e.	cliff	_____	j.	earmuff	_____

Word list

| legs | heads | milk | melted | fresh | jelly | cheese | rice | cake |

15. Learn the spellings. Now look and say, picture, cover, write, check.

_____   _____

_____   _____

_____   _____

_____   _____

_____

16. Write any words you got wrong.

_____

17. Write the missing words. Use the word list.

a.   _____ vegetables are good for you.

b.   Milk is used to make _____.

c.   _____ can be a wobbly dessert.

d.   I only had five pieces of chocolate _____.

e.   They eat a lot of _____ in Japan.

> Oh how kind, they have left me some **cheese**.

18. Use these words to make sentences of your own.

a.   legs   _____

b.   heads   _____

c.   milk   _____

d.   melted _____

19. Write the answers. Use the word list.

a.   Write two plural words from the list. _____ _____

b.   Find smaller words in:

melted _____ **cheese** _____ **rice** _____

c.   Write a word that has two syllables. _____

d.   Write three words that have a silent **e**.

_____ _____ _____

e.   Change one letter in each of these words to make words from the list.

dice _____ **mill** _____ **logs** _____

Drama

20. Work with a group. Recite the menu poem with different people saying different parts. Make the meals sound delicious. Write out your own part.

Write about

21. Write a simple menu with one dish under each heading. It can be real food or imaginary dishes. Give your restaurant a name and remember to add a price. Do your rough work below.

Starter: _____

Main Course: _____

Dessert: _____

Cost: _____

22. Type out your menu. Put all the menus together to form a class booklet.

23. Change the underlined words for a rhyming word to make a new menu. Write the new menu in your copybook.

Starters

Hot <u>broth</u> with fruity <u>chunks</u>

Main courses

<u>Pork</u> and <u>rice</u> served with <u>peas</u>
Grilled <u>steak</u> sprinkled with <u>cheese</u>
Selection of baked <u>pies</u>

Desserts

<u>Fudge</u> ice-cream
<u>Pear</u> tart and cream
Chocolate <u>log</u>

flies
frog
bees
stork
lice
bear

moth
fleas
snake
skunks
sludge

Before you read...

What animals from different countries have you seen?

1. Read the text.

Kangaroos

Kangaroos live in Australia. They have very large back legs which they use for jumping. They also have large, strong tails which they use for balance or to lean on. Kangaroos can hop as fast as fifty kilometres per hour. They cannot walk backwards.

Baby kangaroos are called joeys. They live in their mother's pouch until they are between five and eleven months old. When they are first born, baby kangaroos have no fur. They are just a few centimetres long with two tiny arms. They are blind and helpless.

Male kangaroos are called boomers. They do not have pouches. Female kangaroos are called flyers.

Kangaroos are herbivores. This means they eat only plants. Kangaroos do not need much water. But when it is very hot, they lick their wrists a lot. This makes them cooler.

There are more than fifty kinds of kangaroos, including red kangaroos and grey kangaroos.

This story is a popular myth.
When the first white settlers came to Australia, they had never seen a kangaroo before. It is believed they asked the Aborigines what they were. The Aborigines replied, 'Kanguru,' which means, 'I don't understand you.' From then on, they were known as 'kangaroos'!

A group of kangaroos is called a mob.

2. Talk about.

What would a kangaroo have been called in Irish if people had said 'I don't know'? Talk about wild animals from different countries.

> The late Steve Irwin did much to conserve kangaroos.

3. Answer the questions.

> **Remember** Write full sentences.

a. Where do kangaroos live?

_____

b. What do they use their tails for?

_____

c. Where do baby kangaroos live?

_____

d. When do kangaroos lick their wrists?

_____

e. Name one kind of kangaroo.

_____

f. According to myth what does *Kanguru* mean?

_____

4. Write the answers.

a. How do kangaroos move?

_____

b. Describe what a new born kangaroo looks like.

_____

c. Can a kangaroo move as fast as a tractor?

_____

d. Write a sentence about the kangaroo.

_____

5. Find words in the story with the same meaning.

a. baby kangaroos _____

b. male kangaroos _____

c. animals that eat plants only _____

d. cannot see _____

e. female kangaroos _____

When the letter **c** is followed by **e**, **i** or **y** it usually gives a soft sound.

> **Sample** ceiling

When the letter **c** is followed by **a**, **o** or **u**, it usually gives a hard sound.

> **Sample** camp

6. Circle the words that have a **soft c** sound and underline the words that have a **hard c** sound.

cent	camp	card	coat
race	cone	city	braces
face	cube	fence	cabbage

7. Write the missing letters. Circle the words that have a **soft c** sound.

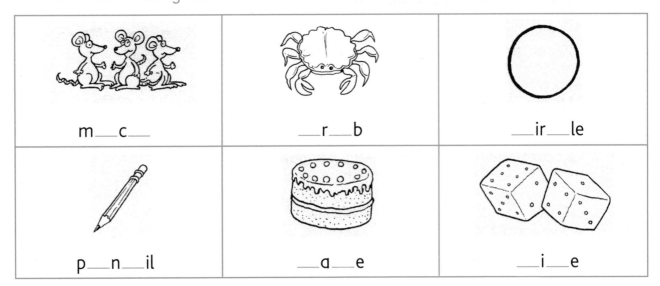

m__c__	__r__b	__ir__le
p__n__il	__a__e	__i__e

8. Underline **c** in these words. Sort the words into **hard c** sounds and **soft c** sounds.

> rice   call   place   car   price   lace   cymbal   crash   cold   candle

Soft **c**	Hard **c**

The camel eats cereal.

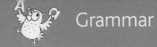
Prepositions link nouns in a sentence and often say where things are.

> **Sample** under, next to, between.

Prepositions can also be about time and place.

> **Sample** after, before, until.

9. Underline and then write the prepositions.

   a. The teacher chased me down the hill. _____
   b. Brad is under the table. _____
   c. Humpty sat on the wall. _____
   d. The bat flew above her head. _____
   e. Wipe your feet before you come in. _____
   f. My brother swam across the river. _____
   g. Caitríona wanted to sit beside me. _____
   h. We cannot talk during class. _____

10. Complete the sentences using prepositions.

into	without	over	at	up	next to	from	with

   a. There is a monster _____ you.
   b. The dog jumped _____ the cat.
   c. Can I come _____ you to the movies?
   d. Dara jumped _____ the river.
   e. We are _____ school now.
   f. I won't sleep _____ my teddy bear.
   g. My Mum got a letter _____ the teacher.
   h. Do not be afraid to climb _____ the ladder.

   > Can I sit **next to** Sara?

11. Write the paragraph correctly with punctuation marks.

   on wednesday i am having a valentine party all my friends are coming to it i hope that ryan asks me to dance

   _____

   _____

   _____

> **Remember** Full stops and capital letters.

Word list

use	no	only	never	strong	arms	makes	more	red

12. Learn the spellings. Now look and say, picture, cover, write, check.

_____   _____

_____   _____

_____   _____

_____   _____

_____

13. Write any words you got wrong.

_____

14. Write the missing words. Use the word list.

a. There are _____ plants on the moon.

b. _____ your knife and fork at the dinner table.

c. The movie *Dumbo* _____ me cry.

d. Eating spinach will make you _____.

e. Wave your _____ in the air.

> School **makes** me happy.

15. Use these words to make sentences of your own.

a. only   _____

b. never   _____

c. red   _____

d. more   _____

16. Write the answers. Use the word list.

a. Which words from the list have two syllables?

_____

b. Find smaller words in:

use   _____   never   _____

only   _____   more   _____

c. Write the words that begin with **m**.

_____

d Write a word that has a **silent e**. _____

e. Change one letter in each of these words to make words from the list.

rid _____   takes _____

wore _____   string _____

Drama

17. Work with a group. Mime an animal from a different country. The group must guess which animal you are.

Write about

18. Draw and label a kangaroo. In your copybook write five kangaroo facts. Use full sentences.

19. Match the tiles to find eight wild animals.

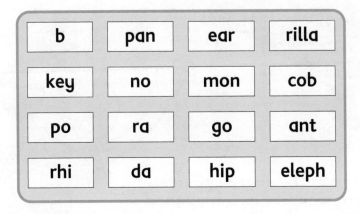

b	pan	ear	rilla
key	no	mon	cob
po	ra	go	ant
rhi	da	hip	eleph

Write the answers here.

_____
_____
_____
_____
_____
_____
_____
_____

20. Make your own tiles of wild animals.

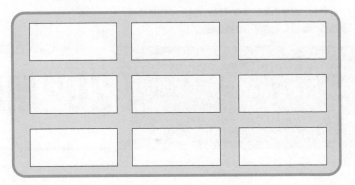

The Australian one dollar coin has kangaroos on it.

 What is the most recent film you have seen?

1. Read the advertisement for the film.

2. Talk about.

How do you think this film ends? Talk about your favourite films.

3. Answer the questions.

Remember to write full sentences.

a. What is the title of the film?

_____

b. What kind of monster stars in the film?

_____

c. Which film company has made the film?

_____

d. How many reviews did the film get?

_____

e. When will it be showing?

_____

4. Write the answers.

a. Why does the monster want revenge?

_____

b. Give the monster a name.

_____

c. Give the boy a name.

_____

d. What do you think happens at the end?

_____

e. Would you watch the film? Explain your answer.

_____

5. Draw a picture for the film.

Sometimes **g** makes a hard sound.

> Sample gift

Sometimes **g** has a soft sound like **j**.

> Sample giant

The **g**iant **g**orilla **g**reeted the **g**iraffe.

6. Circle the words that have a **soft g** sound and underline the words that have a **hard g** sound.

glass	giant	grape	gym
dragon	badge	angel	Germany
glue	giraffe	stag	ghost

7. Write the missing letters. Circle the words with a **soft g** sound.

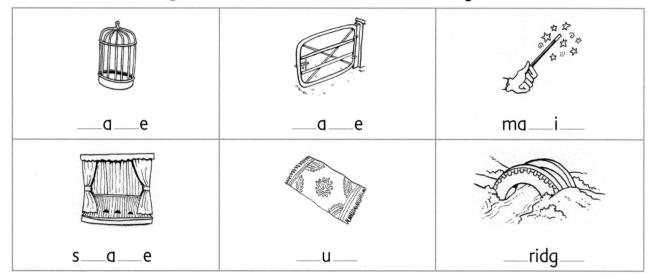

___a__e	___a__e	ma__i__
s__a__e	___u__	___ridg__

8. Underline the **g** in these words. Sort the words into **hard g** sounds and **soft g** sounds.

> age   give   badger   change   flag   ginger   goose   girl

soft **g**	hard **g**

Pronouns are words that are used instead of nouns.

> **Sample** We don't say 'John went to John's house', we say 'John went to **his** house'.

This is all **mine**.

Other pronouns are **I**, **they**, **them**, **he**, **she**, **we**, **us**, **mine**, **it**, **you**, **me**.

9. Underline and then write the pronouns.

   a. I am afraid of bees because they can sting. _____

   b. I don't like this work as it makes me tired. _____

   c. Paul lost his pen so now he wants mine. _____

   d. Please can you make me a cup of tea? _____

   e. When you see the boys tell them to come home. _____

   f. My cat is pretty, but yours is ugly. _____

   g. Our dog always licks its paws. _____

   h. They asked us for ham sandwiches. _____

10. Complete the sentences with pronouns.

    a. I am reading Harry Potter. _____ is exciting.

    b. Kerry invited me to _____ party.

    c. Our family likes chess. _____ play every day.

    d. The lions are hungry. _____ are hunting.

    e. Lisa is good at Maths. _____ loves sums.

> **Remember** Sentences start with a capital letter.

11. Write these sentences in plural form.

    a. The (cat) chased the (leaf).

    _____

    b. The (fairy) gave me three (wish).

    _____

    c. Put the (berry) in the (bowl).

    _____

    d. The (car) are on the (ferry).

    _____

    e. The (bunny) play in the (hutch).

    _____

Word list

monster who trying laugh cry pictures funny kids travel brave

12. Learn the spellings. Now look and say, picture, cover, write, check.

_____   _____
_____   _____
_____   _____
_____   _____
_____   _____

13. Write any words you got wrong.

_____

14. Write the missing words. Use the word list.
   a.   Janet would like to _____ to China.
   b.   We drew pretty _____ of the teacher.
   c.   I am _____ hard to stay awake.
   d.   _____ wants to go home early?
   e.   I am only _____ in the daytime.

15. Use these words to make sentences of your own.
   a.   monster   _____
   b.   laugh   _____
   c.   cry   _____
   d.   funny   _____
   e.   kids   _____

16. Write the answers. Use the word list.
   a.   Write two 2-syllable words from the list.

   _____   _____

   b.   Which word from the list is in plural form?

   _____

   c.   Which words have these words in them?
   try _____   **on** _____
   d.   Underline the letter pattern that is the same
        in these words: **travel**   **brave**
        (Example: **c**o**me**, h**ome**)
   e.   Write the words with three letters. _____

The **monster** under my bed always hides away.

Drama

17. Work with a group. Discuss and act a scene that could be in the film *The chocolate monster*. Make sure everyone has a role to play.

18. Stay in your group to act out some well known superheroes.

Write about

19. Create an advertisement for a film you have seen. Remember to make it look exciting. Display your advert. Do your rough work here.

> Some top children's films are:
> *ET*, *Harry Potter*, *Babe*, *Finding Nemo* and *Toy story*

20. The film titles are mixed up. Write the titles correctly.

   a. The lion wars _____

   b. A shark's hedge _____

   c. Home tale _____

   d. Star Kong _____

   e. Finding age _____

   f. Ice yard _____

   g. Barn king _____

   h. The little Nemo _____

   i. King alone _____

   j. Over the mermaid _____

 What colour and length is your hair?

1.   Read the text.

Ten hairy facts

Some hair-raising facts:

1.   Your body is covered in about five million hairs. The longest are on your head.

2.   Hair keeps you warm! (A bit like fur on an animal!)

3.   Hair is made of a substance called keratin. This is the same stuff that makes feathers, beaks and claws!

4.   Most people have 100,000 hairs on their head.

5.   Your hair grows about one centimetre each month. Hot weather makes your hair grow faster.

6.   You lose fifty or more hairs every day.

7.   Hair is very strong. It is stronger than copper wire of the same thickness.

8.   Hair is dead. Hair roots are alive and they push dead cells up through the scalp. This dead stuff is what you comb and brush!

9.   Your hair stands on end when you're scared because little muscles in the skin pull on the roots of the hairs. The idea is to make you look big and fearsome to an enemy!

10.   Goosebumps are the bumps on your skin which appear when you are cold or frightened. Long ago, people had more hair. If the body got cold, the hairs stood on end. This trapped in air and kept the person warmer. Now people have less hair but the body still reacts to the cold. Little bumps rise where hair use to be thicker and longer.

> People with red hair have the least strands of hair
> but their strands are thicker.

2. Talk about.

Do you think boys should have short hair? Talk about
different hair styles and accepting people for the way they are.

3. Answer the questions.

Remember Write full sentences.

a.   How does hair help you?

_____

b.   What substance is hair made of?

_____

c.   Where else can this substance be found?

_____

d.   How many hairs do you lose every day?

_____

e.   What part of your hair is alive?

_____

f.   When do you get goosebumps?

_____

4. Write the answers.

a.   How much would your hair grow in four days?

_____

b.   Would your hair grow faster in Spain or in Iceland?

_____

c.   What makes your hair stand on end?

_____

d.   What colour hair do you have?

_____

5. Complete the sentences.

a.   Your _____ is covered in hair.

b.   An animal has _____ to keep it warm.

c.   Long ago, _____ had more hair.

d.   Hair is _____ than copper wire.

6. Add **ace** or **age** to make words.

> Notice the **hard** and **soft c** and **g** sounds.

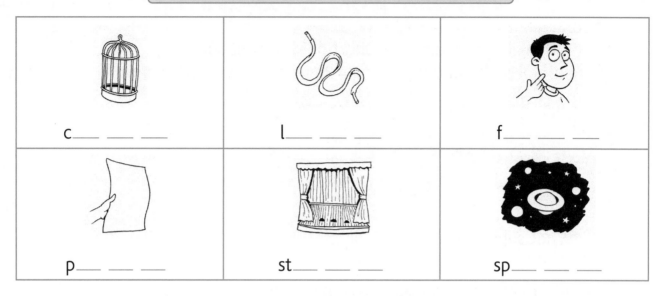

c___ ___ ___   l___ ___ ___   f___ ___ ___

p___ ___ ___   st___ ___ ___   sp___ ___ ___

7. Add **ain** or **air** to make words.

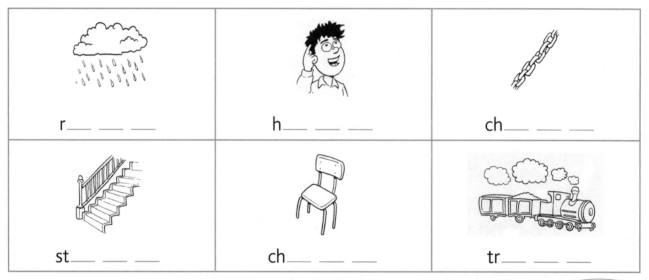

r___ ___ ___   h___ ___ ___   ch___ ___ ___

st___ ___ ___   ch___ ___ ___   tr___ ___ ___

8. Make words. Circle the nonsense words.

	Add **ace**.	Add **age**.	Add **ain**.	Add **air**.
p –	_____	_____	_____	_____
st –	_____	_____	_____	_____
pl –	_____	_____	_____	_____
f –	_____	_____	_____	_____
tr –	_____	_____	_____	_____

> There is **space** for you in my **cage**.

> There is a **train** in my **hair**.

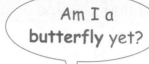

A compound word is a word that is made up of two words

Sample sunshine

Am I a **butterfly** yet?

9. Complete the word sums.

a. air + _____ = airport

b. dust + bin = _____

c. _____ + end = weekend

d. news + _____ = newspaper

e. post + box = _____

f. _____ + noon = afternoon

10. Match the words to make compound words.
Use them to complete the sentences.

| ground father some break stick where play fast broom grand |

a. You should eat _____ in the mornings.

b. The witch fell off her _____

c. My homework must be _____.

d. Jake's _____ tells great stories.

e. The _____ is full of children.

11. Add prepositions to make sentences.

Do not forget the full stops.

a. Colm lives Carlow

_____

b. My socks are the desk

_____

c. The monkey climbed the roof

_____

d. The monster ran the road

_____

e. Leave your bag the door

_____

Word list

body	same	fur	push	skin	hair	you	fifty	stands	less

12. Learn the spellings. Now look and say, picture, cover, write, check.

_____   _____

_____   _____

_____   _____

_____   _____

_____   _____

13. Write any words you got wrong.

_____

14. Write the missing words. Use the word list.

a. My rabbit has soft _____.

b. Luke's _____ is very long.

c. My shirt is the _____ as yours.

d. Help me _____ the car out of the mud.

e. Will _____ do my homework for me?

15. In your copybook use these words to make sentences of your own:

body, **skin**, **fifty**, **stands** and **less**.

> Of course I brushed my **hair**.

16. Write the answers. Use the word list.

a. Find smaller words in:

hair _____   skin _____

same _____   fifty _____

push _____   stands _____

b. Write two 1-syllable words from the list. _____

c. Write two words from the list that end in **y**.

_____

d. Do the words that end in **y** sound the same?

_____

e. Write the 3-letter words from the list.

_____

f. Write a word that has two vowels. _____

Drama

17. Work with a friend. Act out a scene at the hairdresser's or barber's between the customer and the hairdresser or barber. Swap roles.

Write about

18. In your copybook write a concrete poem about hair. It should be four lines long and does not have to rhyme. A concrete poem looks like the topic you are talking about. Look at this example.

19. Follow the letter clues to find two types of body covering.

My first is in **nest** but not in **tent**.
My second is in **crab** but not in **bark**.
My third is in **flag** but not in **golf**.
My fourth is in **glue** but not in **huge**.
My fifth is in **pest** but not **stop**.
My sixth is in **sent** but not in **dent**.

My first is in **leaf** but not in **sale**.
My second is in **eat** but not in **bat**.
My third is in **water** but not in **tower**.
My fourth is in **cart** but not in **race**.
My fifth is in **bath** but not in **table**.
My sixth is in **ice** but not in **sick**.
My seventh is in **trap** but not in **tape**.
My eighth is in **shoe** but not in **hope**.

Answer. _____

Answer. _____

Babies haven't any hair:
Old men's heads are just as bare;
From the cradle to the grave
Lies a haircut and a shave.

Samuel Goodman Hoffenstein

How do you get to school?

The first men to fly a plane were the Wright brothers.

1. Read the table.

	Number of wheels	Can carry more than 2	Children can drive/ride	Requires a helmet	Requires fuel	Is used in a sport
car	4	yes	no	no	yes	yes
bus	4	yes	no	no	yes	no
motorbike	2	no	no	yes	yes	yes
skateboard	4	no	yes	yes	no	yes
boat	0	yes	no	no	yes	yes
truck	4+	yes	no	no	yes	no
tractor	4	no	no	no	yes	no
hot air balloon	0	yes	no	no	yes	yes
train	50+	yes	no	no	yes	no
aeroplane	2+	yes	no	no	yes	yes
bicycle	2	no	yes	yes	no	yes
tricycle	3	no	yes	no	no	no
horse	0	no	yes	yes	no	yes

2. Talk about.

Talk about different types of transport. What would you like to drive or ride? Why is safety gear important when you are cycling or skateboarding?

3. Answer the questions.

a. Which form of transport has the most wheels?

_____

b. How many forms of transport do not require fuel?

_____

c. What safety item do you need to ride a horse?

_____

d. Can you name a form of transport children can ride?

_____

e. Can you name one form of transport not used in a sport?

_____

4. Look at the table and write a full sentence about each form of transport.

a. bus _____

b. truck _____

c. train _____

d. hot air balloon _____

e. tricycle _____

5. Tick the sentences that are true. Write them in your copybook.

a. An aeroplane requires fuel.

b. Trains are used in a sport.

c. A bus has two wheels.

d. Children can ride a bicycle.

e. Wear a helmet if you skateboard.

f. A car does not require fuel.

g. Boat racing is a sport.

h. A bicycle has more wheels than a tractor.

i. A car can carry more than two people.

j. You need a helmet when you are on a train.

6. Circle the correct word.

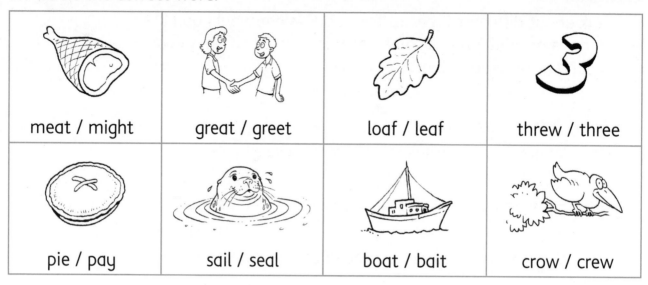

meat / might	great / greet	loaf / leaf	threw / three
pie / pay	sail / seal	boat / bait	crow / crew

7. Write the missing sounds. Read the sentences.

The **owl** and the pussy cat went to **sea** in beautiful **pea**-green boat.

ay	ee	igh	ow	ew

a.   We sl___ ___p at n___ ___ ___t.

b.   Thr___ ___ your rubbish aw___ ___.

c.   The bird fl___ ___ h___ ___ ___ in the sky.

d.   Did you s___ ___ the sh___ ___?

e.   I m___ ___ ___t pl___ ___ football.

f.   I dr___ ___ a buzzing b___ ___.

g.   We ate lamb st___ ___ tod___ ___.

h.   Please m___ ___ the gr___ ___n grass.

8. Underline **c** and **g** in these words. Sort the words and write them in the table.

nice	huge	crunch	fudge	brag	space
grin	cat	goat	crazy	trace	judge

soft **c**	hard **c**	soft **g**	hard **g**

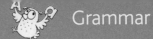

9. Write the sentences correctly.

    Remember Punctuation marks.

    a. mrs. bean is leaving for cavan on monday

    _____

    b. last week i read a book about england

    _____

    c. in july we travelled to paris in france

    _____

    d. we remember saint brigid in february

    _____

    e. megan and killian left for rome in october

    _____

    f. caroline and i are going shopping in longford

    _____

10. Write the words in plural form.

    elf   _____   box   _____
    class   _____   calf   _____
    pony   _____   army   _____
    wheel   _____   branch   _____
    wolf   _____   wish   _____

11. Write the correct pronouns.

    The teacher teaches **us** English. **We** love **it**.

    a. Michael is kind. _____ did my homework
        for me.
    b. I have lost my socks so can I borrow _____?
    c. When William phones, tell _____ to come over.
    d. The house is very old. _____ could fall down.
    e. My friend and I are bored. _____ want to go home.
    f. Mary has many pets. _____ loves animals.
    g. The boys were caught talking. _____ have to stay in at break.
    h. The children left _____ coats in the hall.

Word list

| yes drive used bus boat truck train horse number carry sport |

11. Learn the spellings. Now look and say, picture, cover, write, check.

_____   _____

_____   _____

_____   _____

_____   _____

_____   _____

_____

12. Write any words you got wrong.

_____

13. Write the missing words. Use the word list.

> An ant can **carry** more than 30 times its own weight.

   a.   My dad will _____ me to school.

   b.   Horse-racing is a kind of _____.

   c.   Joe will _____ the teacher's books.

   d.   Flour is _____ to bake a cake.

   e.   The _____ was far out at sea.

   f.   The _____ has a black mane and tail.

14. In your copybook use these words to make sentences of your own:
    yes, **bus**, **truck**, **train** and **number**.

15. Write the answers. Use the word list.

   a.   Find smaller words in:

   used _____   **horse** _____   **bus** _____

   carry _____   **train** _____   **sport** _____

   b.   Write two 2-syllable words from the word list.

   _____

   c.   Write the words that have an **s**.

   _____

   d.   Write the first five words in alphabetical order.

   _____

   e.   Underline a letter pattern that is the same in these words:
        sport   **horse**

Drama

16. Recite the poem.

Where Mum drives me

She drives me batty
She drives me to the edge
She drives me bonkers
She drives me off my head.

She drives me potty
She drives me to the end
She drives me gaga
She drives me round the bend.

She drives me loopy
She drives me till I jump
She drives me bananas
She drives me off my chump

She drives me crazy
She drives me up the wall
She drives me scatty
And she drives me to school.

Steve Turner

BMX stands for Bicycle Moto Cross.

Write about

17. In your copybook draw and fill in a table using the same headings as the table on page 40. Use these forms of transport: **rollerblades**, **helicopter**, **parachute**, **scooter**, **go-cart**, **jeep**, **ship**, **sleigh**, **jet ski** and **camel**.

18. Find all the transport words.

t	a	w	r	r	s	l	e	i	g	h	e
r	s	a	u	n	b	g	b	c	d	j	i
a	u	h	e	l	i	c	o	p	t	e	r
i	s	o	i	e	c	a	a	c	v	e	b
n	m	r	l	p	y	r	t	k	j	p	h
b	u	s	g	s	c	o	o	t	e	r	f
d	g	e	a	q	l	w	y	t	p	o	i
t	s	k	a	t	e	b	o	a	r	d	u

skateboard	bicycle	ship	train
boat	car	jeep	bus
helicopter	scooter	sleigh	horse

 Before you read...

How are you feeling today?

1. Read the poem.

Feelings

I'm as happy as an elephant,
   rolling in the mud,
I'm as excited as a shark,
   smelling fishy blood,
I'm as lonely as a camel,
   walking on desert sands,
I'm as frightened as a bird,
   cupped in your hand,
I'm as joyful as a bee,
   on a sweet and pretty flower,
I'm as cheerful as a hippo,
   in a mid-September shower,
I'm as sad as a donkey,
   left in a field alone,
I'm as surprised as a puppy,
   with a giant, juicy bone,
I'm as angry as a cat,
   when the mouse got away,
I'm as weary as a fruit bat,
   who's upside down all day.

I have so many feelings,
but I think I'll pick just one,
I think I'll choose the elephant,
he's having the most fun!

Are you as pleased
as punch to be at school?

2. Talk about.

    Discuss the different feelings we may have during the day.
    What makes you feel happy, sad, bored or excited?

3. Answer the questions.

    a.   Which animal is cheerful?

    _____

    b.   Why is the cat angry?

    _____

    c.   Where is the camel walking?

    _____

    d.   What can the shark smell?

    _____

    e.   Why is the donkey sad?

    _____

    f.   What is the weather like for the hippo?

    _____

4. Write the answers.

    a.   What do you think the bee is doing on the flower?

    _____

    b.   Name three feelings the poet is having.

    _____

    c.   Who do you think the donkey might belong to?

    _____

    d.   Who do you think is having the best time? Explain your answer.

    _____

5. Find words in the story with the same meaning.

       Use your dictionary.

    a.   tired   _____   f.   strolling   _____
    b.   afraid   _____   g.   amazed   _____
    c.   heartbroken   _____   h.   attractive   _____
    d.   cross   _____   i.   huge   _____
    e.   glad   _____   j.   meadow   _____

6. Write the missing letters.

or	ar

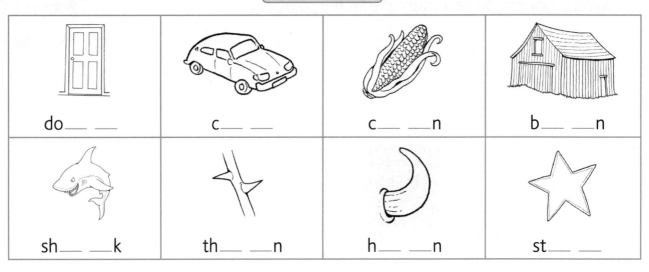

| do__ __ | c__ __ | c__ __n | b__ __n |
| sh__ __k | th__ __n | h__ __n | st__ __ |

7. Circle the correct words. Write the sentences.

   a.   Please close the (door / dart) when you leave.

   _____

   b.   The (fork / farm) has many animals.

   _____

   c.   I would like some (mark / more) peas please.

   _____

   d.   The opposite of tall is (short / sharp).

   _____

   e.   I eat (card / corn) with butter.

   _____

8. Make words. Read the new words.

   Add **or**.   Add **ar**.
   f__ __   f__ __
   f__ __m   f__ __m
   l__ __d   l__ __d
   p__ __k   p__ __k
   c__ __d   c__ __d
   p__ __t   p__ __t
   b__ __n   b__ __n

The shark ate corn with a fork.

Nouns are naming words.
Common nouns are general names of things, people or places.

| Sample town, girls, table, pen |

Proper nouns are the nouns of people, places, months, days of the week, rivers, mountains.

| Sample Rome, Tuesday, June |

Collective nouns are groups of things.

| Sample flock of sheep |

A group of jellyfish
is called a smuck.

9. Use nouns to complete these sentences.
    a. The _____ talked to a _____.
    b. The _____ went down to the _____.
    c. The _____ swim in the _____.
    d. The _____ shouted at the _____.
    e. The _____ swan in the _____.

10. Write the collective nouns.

| litter   bunch   herd   shoal   swarm |

    a. The shark followed the _____ of fish.
    b. I ate a _____ of bananas.
    c. The _____ of bees got closer and closer.
    d. Phil wanted the whole _____ of puppies.
    e. The _____ of cattle are grazing.

A group of crows is called
a murder of crows.

11. Write three nouns for each group.

vegetables   _____   _____   _____
animals   _____   _____   _____
counties   _____   _____   _____
sports   _____   _____   _____
countries   _____   _____   _____

Word list

| mud shark blood bird sweet pretty sad choose walking field puppy |

12. Learn the spellings. Now look and say, picture, cover, write, check.

_____   _____
_____   _____
_____   _____
_____   _____
_____   _____
_____

13. Write any words you got wrong.

_____

14. Write the missing words. Use the word list.

   a.   This honey is very _____.

   b.   My brother got a Dalmatian _____.

   c.   The _____ is full of daffodils.

   d.   _____ is made from earth and water.

   e.   An eagle is a type of _____.

   f.   Go to the library and _____ a book.

Shark!

15. In your copybook use these words to make sentences of your own:
shark, blood, pretty, sad and **walking.**

16. Write the answers. Use the word list.

   a.   Write the words that end with **d**. _____

      _____

   b.   Write a 1-syllable word from the list. _____

   c.   Write a 2-syllable word from the list. _____

   d.   Find smaller words in:

      puppy _____   **shark** _____   **walking** _____

   e.   Write the last five words in alphabetical order.

      _____

Drama

17. Work with a group. Recite the poem from the start of the unit. Use your voice to show the different feelings.

18. Tell the group how you are feeling today. Remember to be kind to others. Do not make fun of other people's feelings.

Write about

19. Complete this simile poem. It does not have to rhyme. Make up your own similes.

> You can change **a** to **an**.

I'm as good as a _____.
As strong as a _____.
As cute as a _____.
And as smart as a _____.

I'm as lovely as a _____.
As nice as a _____.
As fit as a _____.
And as brave as a _____.

As hairy as a _____.
As funny as a _____.
As clever as a _____.
And as _____.

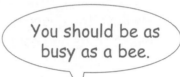

You should be as busy as a bee.

20. Read the poem to yourself and then to your group.

21. Complete the similes.

As angry as a _____.
As dead as a _____.
As free as a _____.
As hairy as a _____.
As happy as a _____.
As hungry as a _____.
As poor as a _____.
As proud as a _____.
As sick as a _____.

I am as strong as an ox.

 Before you read...

What season is it now?

1. Read the story of *Father Frost*.

1. Morozko lived in Russia. He was Father Frost. He brought the icy weather.	2. Morozko was a clever and cruel man. He froze everything he touched. 
3. It was a bitterly cold day. Morozko met a young girl in the woods.  Hello sir. You are Morozko. 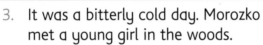	4. Morozko was pleased that the girl was so polite. I am going to reward you for your politeness. Most people fear me.
5. He gave the young girl beautiful warm coats and gold jewels. Thank you, Morozko.  	6. A greedy woman heard about the girl's good fortune. She left her own daughter in the woods so that she could get coats and jewels too. Wait here for Morozko! Make sure he gives you something. We will be rich! 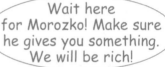 
7. The girl waited for Morozko. She was impatient. Why doesn't he hurry up? 	8. Morozko walked through the woods and saw the girl. Morozko, I have been waiting for you for such a long time! I am cold and hungry! 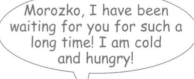
9. Morozko was angry. The girl was rude. He froze her solid. 	10. This story warns people to respect Morozko and the cold weather. If they don't, they will freeze in the winter. 

2. Talk about.

Do you think Morozko was fair? Talk about the
characters in the story. Talk about winter and its effects.

3. Answer the questions.

    a.   Where did Morozko live?

    b.   What did he bring?

    c.   Who did Morozko meet in the woods?

    d.   Why was he pleased?

    e.   What did the young girl receive?

    f.   Who did the greedy woman leave in the woods?

    g.   What happened to her?

4. Answer the questions.

    a.   How did most people feel about Morozko?

    b.   How was he treated by the greedy woman's daughter?

    c.   What is the warning in the story?

5. In your copybook put the sentences in order.

    a.   The girl was polite.
    b.   He froze her solid.
    c.   The greedy woman left her daughter in the woods.
    d.   Morozko met a young girl.
    e.   The daughter was rude to Morozko.
    f.   He gave her gifts.

Er, **ir**, **ur** in the middle of a word usually makes an **ir** sound as in **fir**st.

6. Write the missing letters.

er	ir	ur

 j__ __sey	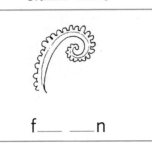 sk__ __t	 ch__ __ch
  g__ __l	 f__ __n	 s__ __f

7. Sort the words.

turn	dirt	perfect	bird	hurt	every	nurse	mermaid	thirty

er	ir	ur

8. Make words. Read the new words.

Add **ur**.

b__ __n   n__ __se
h__ __ley   f__ __
b__ __st   p__ __r
Sat__ __day   t__ __key

The bird got **hurt** while **surfing**.

9. Write a silly sentence using **er**, **ir** and **ur** words from this page.

_____

_____

_____

A verb is an action word.

> **Sample** He **swims** in the lake. He **is** cold.

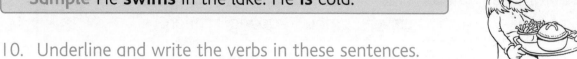

10. Underline and write the verbs in these sentences.

    a. Maggie eats bread with carrots. _____

    b. My brother climbs the tree. _____

    c. The class is happy today. _____

    d. Our teacher smiles all day. _____

    e. Mum cooks pie and chips. _____

    f. My brother plays the drums. _____

    g. I am afraid of thunder. _____

    h. The children were in the tree house. _____

11. Complete the sentences with suitable verbs.

    a. Kieran _____ in the garden.

    b. I always _____ in the classroom.

    c. Rory _____ down the road.

    d. The dog _____ by the door.

    e. The lion _____ hungry.

    f. The doctor _____ in the hospital.

    g. The bird _____ Michelle on her finger.

    h. The teacher _____ a great goal.

> At school we **write, draw, learn, sing, add** and **play.**

12. Choose the correct verb to complete the sentences.

swings	trots	glides	scampers	crawls	hops	swims	waddles

    a. The mouse _____ into its nest.

    b. The duck _____ to the river.

    c. The goldfish _____ around the tank.

    d. The spider _____ across my bed.

    e. The horse _____ around the field.

    f. The monkey _____ by its tail.

    g. The rabbit _____ to its burrow.

    h. The eagle _____ through the air.

Word list

everything	met	gold	woman	here	something	hurry
	such	clever	man	young	angry	

13. Learn the spellings. Now look and say, picture, cover, write, check.

_____   _____

_____   _____

_____   _____

_____   _____

_____   _____

14. Write any words you got wrong.

_____

15. Write the missing words. Use the word list.

a. You do not have to be _____ to do well at school.

b. I must _____ to the office during break.

> Let's get the **gold**.

c. Adam _____ Tim in Dublin.

d. The opposite of old is _____.

e. Mandy has an expensive _____ ring.

f. This is _____ an exciting day.

16. In your copybook use these words to make sentences of your own:
woman, **here**, **everything**, **something**, **man** and **angry**.

17. Write the answers. Use the word list.

a. Break **something** and **everything** into two words.

_____

b. Which words from the list start with:

you _____   **me** _____

he _____   **go** _____

c. Write a 2-syllable word from the list. _____

d. Write a 3-syllable word from the list. _____

e. Change one letter in each of these words to make words from the list:

women _____ **golf** _____ **were** _____

Drama

18. Work with a group. Act out the story of *Father Frost*. Show what happens to the greedy woman.

| The South Pole has no sunshine for 182 days per year. |

Write about

19. Write a winter poem based on the human senses. Make your descriptions interesting. Do your rough work here.

    I see _____
    I smell _____
    I hear _____
    I feel _____
    I taste _____
    I think _____

20. Read through your poem carefully. Improve it if you can. Take away 'I see, I smell, I hear' etc

21. Write out your poem neatly. Make a class anthology of winter poems.

22. Change the word **COLD** to **BEST** by changing one letter at a time.

    COLD
    __ __ __ __ a young horse
    __ __ __ __ latch (door)
    __ __ __ __ keeps trousers up
    __ __ __ __ top

23. Change the word **SNOW** to **FLED** by changing one letter at a time.

    SNOW
    __ __ __ __ not fast
    __ __ __ __ ebb, as in river
    __ __ __ __ past tense of **fly**
    __ __ __ __ ran away

24. In your copybook try changing **FIRE** to **WAND** by changing one letter at a time.

| Most snow crystals have six sides. |

55

What sea creatures have you seen?

Before you read...

1. Read the text.

> The Yangtse dolphin is one of the world's rarest animals.

Dolphins

The dolphin lives in the ocean and eats fish and other small sea animals. It is not a fish. It is a mammal. It breathes air through a blowhole on the top of its head.

The dolphin is a very intelligent animal and has excellent hearing. It can find things in the water by making sounds and listening to the echoes that bounce back.

The largest type of dolphin is the orca or killer whale. It eats sea creatures and smaller dolphins! Other types of dolphin are bottle-nosed dolphins and spinner dolphins.

Dolphins usually live in groups. These groups are called pods. A pod can be anything from a few dolphins to two thousand! If one dolphin in the pod is hurt or ill, the others push it to the surface so that it can still breathe.

There are also stories of dolphins helping humans. They are said to have kept people afloat in the sea and protected them by chasing away sharks.

Dolphins have a language of their own. They use more than thirty-two different sounds to 'talk' to each other.

2. Talk about.

Talk about interesting sea creatures.
How can we stay safe in the sea?
Work with a friend and tell each other about
what you have read.

3. Answer the questions.

    a.   Where does the dolphin live?

    _____

    b.   How does it breathe?

    _____

    c.   Is it a fish? Explain your answer.

    _____

    d.   How do dolphins 'talk' to each other?

    _____

    e.   What does the dolphin eat?

    _____

    f.   How many dolphins are there in a pod?

    _____

    g.   Name one type of dolphin.

    _____

4. Write the answers in your copybook.

    a.   How does the dolphin find things in the water?
    b.   How might one dolphin help another?
    c.   Name one way in which dolphins have helped humans.
    d.   Complete the sentence. Make it interesting!
         Dolphins are _____
    e.   Name one thing that shows the dolphin is clever.

Use dictionaries.

5. Write definitions (meanings) for the words.

    a.   blowhole _____
    b.   orca _____
    c.   pod _____
    d.   protected _____
    e.   intelligent _____

When a word has **tch** only the **ch** sound is heard. The **t** is silent.

> **Sample** stre**tch**

6. Write the missing letters.

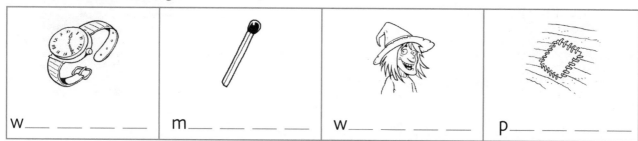

w___ ___ ___   m___ ___ ___ ___   w___ ___ ___ ___   p___ ___ ___ ___

> Use dictionaries to look up words you do not know.

7. Circle the correct words. Write the sentences.

   a.   My cat won't (snatch / scratch) you.

   _____

   b.   A (stitch / switch) in time saves nine.

   _____

   c.   The (pitch / ditch) is too wet to play on.

   _____

   d.   (Catch / Hatch) the ball or we will lose the (watch / match).

   _____

   e.   Close the (fetch / latch) on the (hutch / batch).

   _____

> Don't worry –
> he won't scra**tch**.

8. Make words. Read the new words.
   Add **tch**.

   a.   stre___ ___ ___   d.   fe___ ___ ___
   b.   ki___ ___ ___en   e.   sna___ ___ ___
   c.   cru___ ___ ___es   f.   clu___ ___ ___

9. Write a silly sentence using **tch** words from this page.

   _____

   _____

> **Fetch** the witch's
> cru**tches**.

Adjectives are describing words. They describe nouns.

Sample The **red** parrot was in a **beautiful** cage.

10. Use an adjective to describe each noun.

Do not use: good, bad, big, small. These are used too often.

a. _____ train   f. _____ fish

b. _____ school   g. _____ bedroom

c. _____ boy   h. _____ shirt

d. _____ girl   i. _____ movie

e. _____ meal   j. _____ teacher

11. Write new sentences with adjectives that describe the underlined nouns.

a. The <u>girl</u> has a <u>jumper</u>.

_____

b. My <u>hamster</u> sleeps on my <u>bed</u>.

_____

c. The <u>man</u> buys a <u>pig</u>.

_____

d. Mum makes <u>rice</u> and <u>gravy</u>.

_____

e. The <u>house</u> is next to the <u>tree</u>.

_____

12. Sometimes we compare things, e.g. quick – quicker – quickest. Do the same with these:

light – _____ _____

clean – _____ _____

dark – _____ _____

rich – _____ _____

slow – _____ _____

high – _____ _____

kind – _____ _____

warm – _____ _____

tall – _____ _____

hard – _____ _____

Use adjectives in your own writing.

Word list

fish	ill	top	away	anything	lives
animals	sounds	whale	dolphin	show	ocean

13. Learn the spellings. Now look and say, picture, cover, write, check.

_____   _____

_____   _____

_____   _____

_____   _____

_____   _____

_____   _____

14. Write any words you got wrong.

_____

> The **fish** I caught was this big.

15. Write the missing words. Use the word list.

   a.   She has the flu and feels _____.

   b.   Another word for sea is _____.

   c.   I want to _____ for trout in the river.

   d.   Put your books _____ and have a rest.

   e.   A _____ is the largest sea mammal.

   f.   A cat is said to have nine _____.

16. In your copybook use these words to make sentences of your own:
   top, **anything**, **sounds**, **animals**, **dolphin** and **show**.

17. Write the answers. Use the word list.

   a.   Find smaller words in:

   fish _____   **top** _____   **away** _____   **show** _____

   b.   Write two words from the list that have a **sh** sound.

   _____   _____

   c.   Break this word into two words: **anything**

   _____   _____

   d.   Write a word where **ph** makes a **f** sound. _____

   e.   Write a word where **c** has a **sh** sound. _____

Drama

19. Work with a group. Each person chooses a sea creature and mimes its movements. The group must guess which creature it is.

Write about

20. Research an interesting sea creature. In your copybook write a fact file for the creature and draw a picture. Tell the class about it. Do your rough work here.

21. Can you find smaller words in these sea creatures?

prawn	_____	jellyfish	_____
shark	_____	octopus	_____
haddock	_____	penguin	_____
sunfish	_____	dolphin	_____
seahorse	_____	stingray	_____

A bottle-nosed dolphin can stay under water for 2 hours.

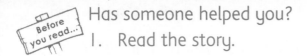

Has someone helped you?
1. Read the story.

The lion and the mouse

An enormous lion was asleep under a tree. A tiny mouse was in a hurry and did not see the lion. It ran right over the lion's paw. The mouse froze with fear. The lion woke up. He stretched out his paw and caught the mouse.

'Please don't eat me, Mr. Lion,' begged the mouse. 'Please let me go. Maybe one day I will be able to help you.'

The lion roared with laughter.

'How could a tiny scrap like you possibly help me?' he asked. 'I am the king of the jungle and you are a small mouse.'

The lion decided to let the mouse go free. He went back to sleep, smiling to himself about what had just happened.

A few days later the mouse heard a roar. It sounded like the lion was in trouble. He found the lion caught in a net. The lion could not escape. The net was held together by a strong rope. The king of the jungle was trapped.

Then he heard a tiny squeak.
'I will try and help you,' said the mouse.

The mouse gnawed through the rope. Soon the rope snapped. The lion was able to shake free of the net.

'Thank you, little mouse. I owe you my life,' said the thankful lion.

'Everybody needs help sometime,' said the mouse. 'The important thing is that we help each other.'

The lion and the mouse became good friends.

> Lions sleep for up to twenty hours a day

2.   Talk about.
     Tell the class about other people that have helped you.

3.   Answer the questions.
     a.   What woke the lion?

     b.   Why did the lion not see the mouse?

     c.   Name one thing the mouse said.

     d.   What did the lion do?

     e.   What sound did the mouse hear a few days later?

     f.   What had happened to the lion?

     g.   What did the mouse do?

     h.   Was the lion grateful? Explain your answer.

4.   Write the answers in your copybook.
     a.   Why do you think the lion let the mouse go free?
     b.   How did the lion feel when he was free?
     c.   Find words in the story with the same meaning:
           very big   very small   chewed
     d.   What is the moral of this story?
     e.   How can the lion ever help the mouse in the future?

5.   Put the sentences in the correct order. Write the sentences in your copybook.
     Draw a picture for one sentence.

     ☐   The mouse helped the lion.
     ☐   The lion let the mouse go free.
     ☐   The lion and the mouse became friends.
     ☐   The lion was trapped.

The letters **dge** make a **j** sound.

> **Sample** lodge

6. Write the missing letters.

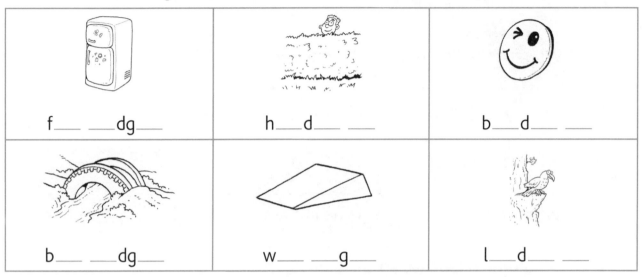

f___ ___dg___	h___d___ ___	b___d___ ___
b___ ___dg___	w___ ___g___	l___d___ ___

> Use a dictionary if you need to.

7. Circle the correct words. Write the sentences.

a. Do not stand on the (ledge / sledge).

_____

b. I will make a (edge / pledge) to do my homework.

_____

c. This sweet (fudge / lodge) is delicious.

_____

d. The cheese is in the (ridge / fridge).

_____

e. This big rock will not (smudge / budge).

_____

8. Make words. Read the new words.
    Add **dge**.
    porri___ ___ ___   tru___ ___ ___
    mi___ ___ ___t   e___ ___ ___
    Bri___ ___ ___t   do___ ___ ___

> Why is Ma**dge** in the fri**dge**?

9. Write a silly sentence with **dge** words.

_____

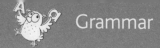

When we write verbs in the past tense, sometimes we add **ed**.

> **Sample** fetch – fetched.

If the verb ends in an **e**, we add just a **d**.

> **Sample** live – lived.

> I **jumped** for joy because it was Friday.

10. Write these words in the past tense.

   a.   wait _____   e.   dive _____
   b.   bake _____   f.   laugh _____
   c.   race _____   g.   work _____
   d.   paint _____   h.   cycle _____

If the verb has a short vowel sound, double the last letter before adding **ed**.

> **Sample** snip – snipped

11. Write these words in the past tense.

   a.   sip   _____   f.   stop _____
   b.   chop _____   g.   slap _____
   c.   rip   _____   h.   slip _____
   d.   pat   _____   i.   trot _____
   e.   grab _____   j.   fit   _____

12. Write these sentences in the past tense.

   a.   We (enjoy) our time on the beach.

   _____

   b.   I (sneeze) very loudly.

   _____

   c.   They (call) the teacher for help.

   _____

   d.   Mum (flip) the pancake into the air.

   _____

   e.   The baby (toss) and (turn) all night.

   _____

   f.   The happy child (skip) and (dance).

   _____

   g.   Mum (drop) the glass and it (shatter).

   _____

   h.   He (rake) up the leaves and (drop) them into the bin.

   _____

Word list

lion	asleep	let	escape	himself	later	tiny	life
everybody	friends	mouse	free	owe			

13. Learn the spellings. Now look and say, picture, cover, write, check.

_____   _____
_____   _____
_____   _____
_____   _____
_____   _____
_____   _____
_____

14. Write any words you got wrong.

_____

15. Write the missing words. Use the word list.

> Do not
> fall **asleep**
> in class.

  a.   Darren can do the sums by _____.
  b.   I hope Mum will _____ me go to school.
  c.   Counting sheep will help you fall _____.
  d.   A baby _____ is called a cub.
  e.   You don't have to pay for the concert as it is
       _____ for children.
  f.   All my _____ are coming for a sleep-over.

16. In your copybook use these words to make sentences of your own:
escape, **tiny**, **life**, **everybody**, **mouse** and **owe**.

17. Write the answers. Use the word list.

  a.   Break **himself** and **everybody** into two words.

  _____

  b.   Find smaller words in these words from the list:
       lion _____ **tiny** _____ **escape** _____ **life** _____
  c.   Write all the 1-syllable words from the list.

  _____

  d.   Write all the 2-syllable words from the list.

  _____

  e.   Write words that have **ee** in them.

  _____

Drama

18. Work with a friend to act out the story of *The lion and the mouse*. Think about your tone of voice, facial expressions and movements.

> Never look on down on anybody unless you're helping him up.

Write about

19. Write the same story but for an Infant class. Remember: words and sentences should be simple, writing should be larger and very clear.

    Do your rough work here. Then write it out neatly, draw a picture and give your stories to the Infant class.

20. Work out the coded message.

A	B	C	D	E	F	G	H	I	J	K	L	M
#	■	%	➤	✳	±	◆	▲	◗	●	❑	★	☆
N	O	P	Q	R	S	T	U	V	W	X	Y	Z
❖	☺	◯	▼	❀	✻	♣	☆	✧	✪	♥	♠	⊥

■✳   ❑◗❖➤   ♣☺   ☺♣▲✳❀✻

_____

21. Use this code to write your own message about showing kindness.

_____

 Name different types of birds that we get in Ireland.

1. Read the poem.

Bird-table blues

In winter, Grandma feeds the birds
With kindly thoughts and friendly words,
And biscuit crumbs, and broken baps,
And bacon rinds, and breakfast scraps,
And plates of freshly buttered toast,
And bags of chips, and Sunday roast,
And dumplings (huge and hot and steamy),
And home-made pies, and gravy (creamy),
And every sort of cheese and bread,
Until each hungry bird is fed
To BURSTING point, to bitter end,
Until their legs begin to bend,
Until they cannot flap or fly,
Until they simply want to die,
Until they roll around the floor
And weakly twitter, 'Stop! No more!'

Then Grandma smiles and says, 'Oh good.
I think they're ready for their pud.'

Clare Bevan

All this work
is for the birds!

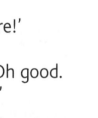

2. Talk about.
    Say whether you liked the poem or not.
    Give reasons for your answer.

3. Answer the questions.

    a. What does Grandma do for the birds in winter?

    _____

    b. What kind of pies does she give them?

    _____

    c. What does she put on the toast?

    _____

    d. Describe the dumplings.

    _____

    e. Name two types of breakfast scraps she feeds them.

    _____

    f. How do the birds feel after eating?

    _____

    g. Write the word for pud.

    _____

4. Answer the questions.

    a. How do you think Grandma feels about the birds?

    _____

    b. Why do you think she feeds them so much food?

    _____

    c. What might Grandma give them for pudding?

    _____

    d. Give the poem another title.

    _____

    e. Why is it a good idea to feed the birds in the winter?

    _____

5. Name two things Grandma gives the birds that you would eat.

    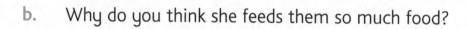

69

6. Write the missing letters.

| ar | or | ir | ur |

| t___ ___ n | st___ ___ | p___ ___ se | j___ ___ |

7. Write your own words with each of these sounds.

_____

8. Circle the correct words. Write the sentences.

> Use a dictionary to look up words you do not know.

a. Conor has to (trudge / fudge) to school in the mornings.

_____

b. That ink will (sledge / smudge) your page.

_____

c. Your school (ridge / badge) has a motto.

_____

d. Did you (dodge / lodge) the ball?

_____

e. The (budge / bridge) goes over the Liffey River.

_____

9. Make words. Circle the nonsense words.

Add tch.
ba___ ___ ___
hu___ ___ ___
sna___ ___ ___
ple___ ___ ___
smu___ ___ ___
wa___ ___ ___

Add dge.
ba___ ___ ___
hu___ ___ ___
sna___ ___ ___
ple___ ___ ___
smu___ ___ ___
wa___ ___ ___

A bird
can't purr!

10. Underline the first letters. Put the words in alphabetical order.

| owl | kingfisher | crow | blackbird | wagtail | swallow |
| lark | thrush | heron | robin | goose |

Jamie keeps little monkeys.

_____   _____

_____   _____

_____   _____

_____   _____

_____

> If all the words start with the same letter, look at the second letter.

11. Underline the second letters. Put the words in alphabetical order.

| beach | ball | bucket | blue | big | bottle | break |

_____   _____

_____   _____

_____

12. Put the words in alphabetical order so they make a sentence.

Remember Punctuation marks.

a. those, eat, vegetables, more, of

_____

b. four, bought, Anita, gifts

_____

c. year, good, be, the, whole

_____

d. do, pets, cats, nice, make

_____

e. we're, parents, think, zany, my

_____

13. Write your own sentence with words in alphabetical order.

_____

Word list

feeds	biscuit	broken	breakfast	sort	point	begin
thoughts	friendly	huge	bitter	toast	roast

14. Learn the spellings. Now look and say, picture, cover, write, check.

_____   _____
_____   _____
_____   _____
_____   _____
_____   _____
_____   _____
_____

15. Write any words you got wrong.

_____

16. Write the missing words. Use the word list.

  a. _____ is an important meal that you should not skip.
  b. The lemon tastes very _____.
  c. Alan _____ his cat every morning.
  d. My pencil has a sharp _____.
  e. I would like a chocolate _____ with my tea.
  f. I have _____ of sitting on a sunny beach.
  g. I cannot ring you as my mobile is _____.

17. In your copybook write your own sentences using these words:
    begin, **huge**, **friendly**, **toast**, **roast** and **sort**.

> Don't worry, these tigers are **friendly**.

18. Write the answers. Use the word list.

  a. Which words contain these words?
      end _____   **it** _____
      or _____   **hug** _____
  b. Write two words that rhyme. _____ _____
  c. Underline the parts of the words that rhyme.
  d. Break this word into two words:
      breakfast = _____ + _____
  e. Think of a mnemonic or rhyme to help you to remember
      to spell **biscuit**.

_____

Drama

19. Work with a partner. Try to remember all the things Grandma fed the birds. Read the poem aloud together to see if you remembered them all.

Write about

20. Write a label poem for a type of bird.
    Your poem does not have to rhyme.

Sample

Name of bird: _____

This creature lives in ... _____

It comes out ... _____

And often ... _____

It is the colour of ... _____

And eats ... _____

Notice how it ... _____

It has a most distinctive cry,

Like ... _____

Beware ... _____

Do not ... _____

Ever.

---

21. In your copybook rewrite the poem neatly. Add a picture and display your poems in the school.

22. How many words can you make from these words?

> PEREGRINE FALCON

_____

_____

_____

A fear of birds
is called ornithophobia.

Unit 13

Do you have a busy week?
1. Read the timetable.

Brian's timetable for May						
Monday	*Tuesday*	*Wednesday*	*Thursday*	*Friday*	*Saturday*	*Sunday*
	1	2	3	4	5	6
	Guitar lessons 4.00pm	Geography test	Maths test	Spelling test		Football match €5.00
7	8	9	10	11	12	13
Chores: clean room	Guitar 4.00pm	Aunt Julie's birthday English test	Band practice – Josh's 5.00pm – 7.00pm	Spelling test Movie on Channel 2		Charlie staying over
14	15	16	17	18	19	20
Chores: garden History test	Guitar 4.00pm Dentist: 3.15pm		Jack's birthday	Spelling test Books to library	Band practice – Darragh's 6.00pm – 8.00pm	Jack's birthday party 3.00 pm
21	22	23	24	25	26	27
Chores: clean room	Guitar 4.30pm	No school	Band practice – Sean's 5.00pm – 7.00pm	Spelling test School finish early – 12.00pm		Fun Fair 6.00pm Match 7.00pm
28	29	30	31			
Chores: garden	No guitar lessons	Band practice – John's 5.00pm – 7.00pm	Science project to be handed in			

There are 86,400 seconds in one day.

2. Talk about.
    Discuss the timetable as a class.
    Do you think Brian has a busy week?

3. Answer the questions.
    a.   How many tests does Brian have in the first week?

    _____

    b.   When does he do his chores?

    _____

    c.   Who is staying over on the 13th?

    _____

    d.   Where is band practice on the 24th?

    _____

    e.   On what channel is the movie Brian wants to watch?

    _____

    f.   How much will the football match cost?

    _____

    g.   What does Brian have every Friday?

    _____

    h.   How many times a month does the band practise?

    _____

4. Write the answers in your copybook.
    a.   How many days after Jack's birthday is his party?
    b.   What instrument do you think Brian plays in the band?
    c.   Do you think he will make his guitar lesson on the 15th?
         Explain your answer.
    d.   Which day do you think sounds the most enjoyable?

5. Work out how many times Brian does these activities in May.
    tests -   _____   visits to the dentist -   _____
    chores -   _____   projects -   _____
    guitar lessons -   _____   birthdays -   _____
    sports events -   _____   funfairs -   _____
    library visits -   _____   parties -   _____

6. Write the missing letters.

oy   oi

c___n	b___ ___	j___ ___
b___ ___l	t___ ___s	s___ ___l

7. Circle the correct words. Write the sentences.

a. Put the (coil / soil) in the flowerpot.

_____

b. I (enjoy / annoy) watching TV.

_____

c. You must (join / joint) the Lego pieces.

_____

d. Dad will (broil / spoil) me for my birthday.

_____

e. My friend is (royal / loyal) to me.

_____

8. Make words. Circle the nonsense words.

Add **oil**.
b___ ___ ___
c___ ___ ___
f___ ___ ___
j___ ___ ___
t___ ___ ___

Add **oy**.
b___ ___
c___ ___
f___ ___
j___ ___
t___ ___

Do not annoy the koi-koi.

9. Write a silly sentence using **oi** and **oy** words.

_____

_____

10. Read the poem. Write eight nouns from the poem.

Stuck in the middle of the afternoon

It's just gone two and it's not yet three
It's way past lunch but it's not yet tea
It's not yet home but it will be soon
I'm stuck in the middle of the afternoon.

It's just gone sshh and it's not yet noise
It's way past books but it's not quite toys
It's bye bye sun but it's not yet moon
I'm stuck in the middle of the afternoon.

It's just gone work and it's not yet play
It's way past start but it still says stay
It's not yet go but it will be soon
I'm stuck in the middle of the afternoon.

Steve Turner

Nouns

11. Read the adjectives. Sort them under the headings.

orange   enormous   square   bored   black   grumpy
tiny   round   medium   green   cheerful   triangular

Shapes	Colours	Moods	Sizes

12. Write these sentences in the past tense.

a. She (trip) over the school bag.

_____

b. Jessie (rake) the leaves for pocket money.

_____

c. The teachers (nap) in the staffroom.

_____

d. The class (love) writing sentences.

_____

e. He (shop) in the local supermarket.

_____

Word list

| test spelling match birthday books garden finish clean |
| History Geography Science Maths English channel |

13. Learn the spellings. Now look and say, picture, cover, write, check.

_____   _____
_____   _____
_____   _____
_____   _____
_____   _____
_____   _____
_____   _____

14. Write any words you got wrong.

_____

15. Write the missing words. Use the word list.

> I did not learn for my **test** because my favourite programme was on TV.

a. In _____ we learn times tables.

b. Dad always watches the sports _____.

c. A library is full of _____.

d. In _____ we learn about rivers.

e. The rugby _____ was exciting.

f. In _____ we learn about animals.

g. We cannot talk during a _____.

h. There is an elephant in my _____.

16. In your copybook use these words to make sentences of your own:
spelling, **birthday**, **finish**, **clean**, **History** and **English**.

17. Write the answers. Use the word list.

a. Break **birthday** into two smaller words.

_____

b. Think of a mnemonic to remember the spelling of **Science**.

_____

c. Find smaller words in these words from the list:

match _____   **channel** _____

finish _____   **Geography** _____

d. Write a 2-syllable word from the list. _____

e. Underline a silent letter in **Science**.

Drama

18. Work with a group. Recite the poem *Stuck in the middle of the afternoon*. Discuss your own week with the group.

Write about

19. Write your own timetable.

My timetable for the week						
Monday	Tuesday	Wednesday	Thursday	Friday	Saturday	Sunday

> Time is the coin of your life. It is the only coin you have, and only you can determine how it will be spent. Be careful lest you let other people spend it for you.
>
> *Carl Sandberg*

20. Fill in the timetable. Change one letter in each underlined word to find each day's activity.

Monday – play <u>gold</u>   Tuesday – go to <u>down</u>
Wednesday – <u>bike</u> muffins   Thursday – <u>Moths</u> test
Friday – <u>road</u> a book   Saturday – <u>sweep</u> in bed
Sunday – sing with the <u>chair</u>

Monday	Tuesday	Wednesday	Thursday	Friday	Saturday	Sunday

Name some road signs you know.

1. Look at the map.

2. Talk about.
   Talk about these funny signs.

3. Answer the questions.
   a. What is the name of the town?

   _____

   b. How far away is the city centre?

   _____

   c. What sporting facility does the town have?

   _____

   d. Where could you have a meal?

   _____

   e. What is the speed limit in town?

   _____

   f. Where would you find the petrol station?

   _____

4. Write the answers in your copybook.
   a. Where is the car park?
   b. Describe which house is for sale.
   c. Is there a recycling centre? Explain your answer.
   d. What public transport is available?
   e. Write directions from the school to the bridge.
   f. How is the town different to yours?

5. In your copybook draw these signs and write their meanings.

6. Write the missing letters.

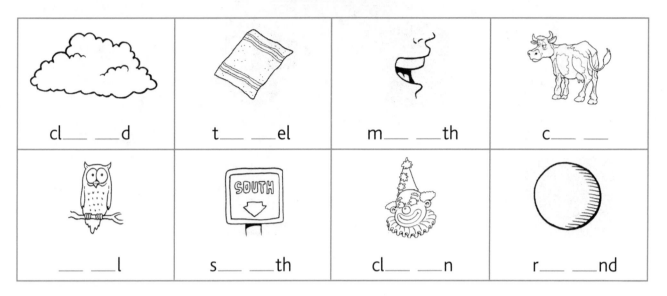

| ow | ou |

cl___ ___d

t___ ___el

m___ ___th

c___ ___

___ ___l

s___ ___th

cl___ ___n

r___ ___nd

7. Circle the correct words. Write the sentences.

a. The lion will (shout / growl) at you.

_____

b. At last I (found / frown) my pen.

_____

c. Take a (shout / shower) to remove that mud.

_____

d. Your voice is too (loud / lout).

_____

e. The (cloud / clown) was acting silly.

_____

8. The **ow** sound can make different sounds. Sort the words by their sound.

| crow | brown | gown | know | howl | show | how | flow |

ow as in **now**	**ow** as in **blow**

Sometimes we add **ing** to a word

> **Sample** jump – jumping

If a words ends in **e**, drop the **e** before adding **ing**.

9. Make new words. Add **ing**.

a. have - _____   f. laugh - _____
b. drive - _____   g. wake - _____
c. sing - _____   h. write - _____
d. watch - _____   i. like - _____
e. rest - _____   j. strike - _____

When a word has a short vowel sound, double the last letter before adding **ing**.

> **Sample** stop – stopping

He is **running** away from the ghost.

10. Make new words. Add **ing**.

a. sip - _____   f. shop - _____
b. hit - _____   g. get - _____
c. swim - _____   h. sit - _____
d. skip - _____   i. chop - _____
e. dig - _____   j. clap - _____

11. Change the words in brackets to **ing** words. Write the new sentences.

a. Ben is (sit) and (read) his comic.

_____

b. They are (sing) while the teacher is (talk).

_____

c. Susie is (hide) and Mum is (call) her.

_____

d. She is (pat) and (ride) the horse.

_____

e. They are (slip) and (fall) on the ice.

_____

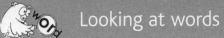
Word list

danger	entry	sale	staff	private	road	ahead
exit	bank	café	closed	speed	welcome	property

12. Learn the spellings. Now look and say, picture, cover, write, check.

_____ _____

_____ _____

_____ _____

_____ _____

_____ _____

_____ _____

_____ _____

13. Write any words you got wrong.

_____

14. Write the missing words. Use the word list.

a.   Your money is safe in the _____ .

b.   We _____ visitors to the school.

c.   My friend lives down the _____ .

d.   Keep out of _____ at all times.

e.   Mum had a cup of coffee at the _____ .

f.   The school is _____ on weekends.

g.   Do not go onto _____ property.

15. In your copybook use these words to make sentences of your own:
entry, **sale**, **staff**, **ahead**, **exit**, **speed** and **property**.

16. Write the answers. Use the word list.

a.   Count the syllables in these words from the list:

welcome _____   **ahead** _____

danger _____   **property** _____

entry _____   **bank** _____

b.   Write a word from the list that has soft **g**. _____

c.   Write the first five words in alphabetical order.

_____

d.   Change one letter in each word to make words from the list:

salt _____   **band** _____   **read** _____

e.   Write a word with double letters. _____

Drama

17. Work with a friend. Pretend to be a tourist asking for directions to somewhere from the school. Swap roles.

Write about

18. Make a sign for a classroom rule.
    Do your rough work here then create the
    sign on the computer and print it out.
    Display your signs in the classroom.
    Make them clear and eye-catching!

19. Follow the directions to find the treasure.

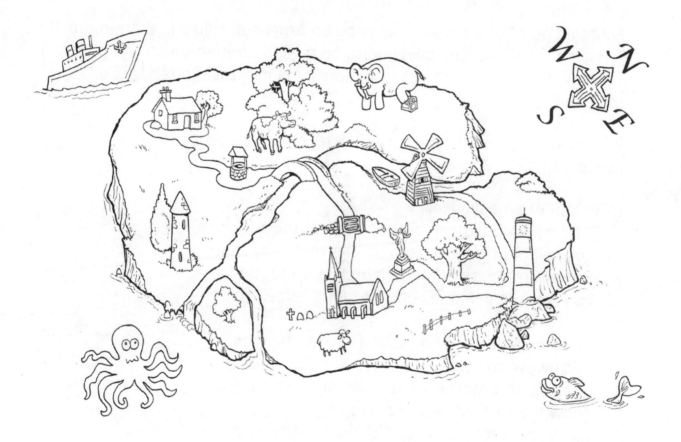

Example:

1. Start at the house in the top left hand corner and walk towards the well.
2. Go over the bridge and keep on the path.
3. Pass through the gate and walk towards the church.
4. Go left to the statue.
5. Walk east towards the tree.

6. Walk to the lighthouse. (Dip your toes into the sea.)
7. Head for the windmill. Pick up your boat.
8. Go across the river.
9. Find a wild animal.
10. Look under his left back foot.

Are you writing in pen yet?

1. Read the text.

Pens

The first pens were used by the Egyptians in about 3500BC. They were made from hollow reeds and the ink was a mixture of soot and water.

In about 700AD, quill pens were made from feathers. These were sharpened at the end. A person would have to keep dipping the pen into ink. Goose feathers were often used.

Fountain pens were made in 1884 by an American called L. Waterman. These pens held ink and only had to be refilled after writing a few pages. Writing with these could be quite messy and ink would often leak all over the page.

Ballpoint pens were invented in 1938 by a man called Lazlo Biro. We mostly use this kind of pen today.

How to make a quill pen:
1. Find a strong feather. You can collect these yourself or buy them from an arts and craft shop.
2. Cut away some of the feathery bits. Hold it as you would a pen and cut away until it feels comfortable.
3. Stick the feather in hot sand. (The teacher can microwave this for you.) Leave it in the sand for an hour. This makes the tube harder and tougher.
4. Allow the feather to cool down.
5. Use scissors to cut the end of the feather with a sloping cut. Make a tiny slit in the longer side.
6. Shape it carefully with your scissors.
7. Dip it into ink and write away!

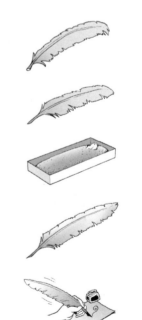

In its first year of being on sale, 53 million biro pens were sold.

2. Talk about.
   What do you like to write with? Besides school, when else do we write?

3. Answer the questions.
   a. When were the first pens used?

   _____

   b. What were the first pens made from?

   _____

   c. What were quill pens made from?

   _____

   d. Why were fountain pens messy?

   _____

   e. Who invented ballpoint pens?

   _____

   f. When were they invented?

   _____

4. Write the missing words.
   a. In Ancient Egypt _____ was made from soot and water.
   b. _____ feathers were often used to make quill pens.
   c. To write with a quill pen you have to keep _____ it into ink.
   d. Fountain pens would have to be _____ after a few pages.
   e. L. Waterman came from _____.
   f. Today we mostly use _____ pens.

5. Write the sentences in the correct order.
   Use scissors to cut and shape the end.
   Write with your pen.
   Cut off the feathery bits.
   Dip your pen into ink.
   Leave the feather in hot sand.

   a. _____
   b. _____
   c. _____
   d. _____
   e. _____

6. Write the missing letters.

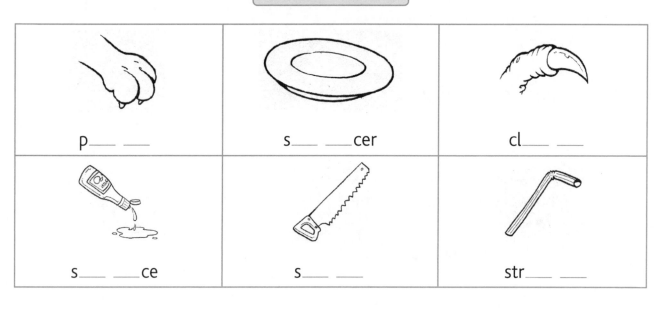

| aw | au |

p__ __

s__ __cer

cl__ __

s__ __ce

s__ __

str__ __

7. The **aw** and **au** words are in the wrong sentences. Underline them and then write the sentences correctly.

a. The teacher gets mad if we sauce.

_____

b. I am not a raw child.

_____

c. I like red yawn on my burger.

_____

d. You cannot eat that naughty meat.

_____

8. Make words. Read the new words.
   Add **aw**.
   h__ __k   l__ __n   d__ __n
   th__ __   str__ __   __ __ful

The teacher taught us how to yawn.

9. Make two silly sentences using **aw** and **au** words from this page.

_____

_____

_____

_____

Antonyms are opposites.

Sample dark – light

10. Write antonyms for these words.

| wide sick pull straight cloudy up difficult grumpy sweet awake |

a. push   _____   f. asleep   _____
b. cheerful _____   g. easy   _____
c. sunny   _____   h. down   _____
d. narrow   _____   i. well   _____
e. sour   _____   j. crooked   _____

11. Write the sentences using antonyms for the underlined words.

| cheap   huge   dislike   buy   messy   warm |

a. I <u>like</u> cabbage on toast.

_____

b. The kitten is <u>cool</u> by the fire.

_____

c. Glenda will <u>sell</u> some Maths books.

_____

d. My new runners were <u>expensive</u>.

_____

e. The <u>tiny</u> rat ran under my <u>neat</u> bed.

_____

12. Write the sentences correctly.
Be careful – you may need to write two sentences.

a. my friend is called lucy we love going to dublin on fridays

_____

b. why can't i come with you to london i will be very good

_____

c. mr. and mrs. noodle will visit italy at easter time

_____

d. matt and ian are going to croke park to watch the match

_____

Word list

| scissors | tougher | mixture | ink | often | writing | pages | today | buy |
| leave | shape | person | hour | longer | feathers |

13. Learn the spellings. Now look and say, picture, cover, write, check.

_____   _____

_____   _____

_____   _____

_____   _____

_____   _____

_____   _____

_____

14. Write any words you got wrong.

_____

15. Write the missing words. Use the word list.

How much **longer** do we have to **write**?

a. _____ are used for cutting.

b. The cake _____ tasted delicious.

c. We _____ play games at break time.

d. The teacher wants me to write three _____ about frogs.

e. My printer has run out of _____.

f. A rectangle is a _____.

g. You should _____ your muddy boots outside.

h. Sixty minutes is one _____.

16. In your copybook use these words to make sentences of your own.
     writing, **today**, **buy**, **tougher**, **feathers**, **person** and **longer**.

17. Write the answers. Use the word list.

a. Write three 2-syllable words from the list.

     _____

b. Find smaller words in these words from the list:
     ink ____ **often** ____ **feathers** ____ **person** ____ **today** ____

c. Write one word in plural form. _____

d. How many 3-letter words are there? _____

Drama

18. Work with a group. Each person must act out a scene where writing is involved. The group must guess what the person is writing.

Write about

19. Write instructions for an activity. Choose something simple like making a sandwich, getting ready for school or tidying your room.

1. _____

2. _____

3. _____

4. _____

5. _____

6. _____

> Early inks were made from plant dyes.

20. Check your instructions and improve them if you can. Write out the final version, add a drawing and display the instructions in the classroom.

21. Build your own wordsearch with these words. Ask a friend to work it out.

> pencil marker biro feather crayon chalk paint ink quill ballpoint

How many superheroes can you name?

1. Read the poem.

The greatest of them all

You can keep your superheroes
Like Batman and the rest –
My dad can beat 'em all hands down,
He really is the best.

He tears up toilet tissues,
He can break a twig in two,
He can lift a bag of feathers,
No, there's nothing he can't do.

He can bend a piece of cardboard,
He can frighten new-born flies,
And at snapping off a daisy head
He always takes first prize.

He's stronger than a sparrow
And he's faster than a snail,
He can punch a hole in newspapers
And never ever fail.

He's thinner than a matchstick
And his biceps look like peas,
His legs are like a spider's
And he's got two knobbly knees.

He's a legend in his lifetime
He's a hero through and through.
And what's the name we know him by?
It's *Superwimp* – that's who!

Clive Webster

Spiderman's real name is Peter Parker.

2. Talk about.
   Talk about family and how important it
   is to accept others the way they are.

3. Answer the questions.

   a. Who is the poet writing about?

   _____

   b. What can he break?

   _____

   c. What can he lift?

   _____

   d. What does he frighten?

   _____

   e. Where does he punch holes?

   _____

   f. What is he known as?

   _____

   g. Which superhero is mentioned in the poem?

   _____

   h. Name a flower in the poem.

   _____

4. Write the answers.

   a. Is the hero in the poem strong? Explain your answer.

   _____

   b. Write two facts about the hero's appearance.

   _____

   c. What does the poet think of this person?

   _____

   d. What is the poet's name?

   _____

5. In your copybook write these sentences.
   Draw a picture to match each one.

   a. He tears up toilet tissue.
   b. He's faster than a snail.
   c. He's thinner than a matchstick.

6. Write the missing letters.

| oo | ue | ew |

m____ ____n

que____ ____

st____ ____

gl____ ____

h____ ____t

n____ ____

7. Write the missing sounds.

| oo | ue | ew |

Do not dr**oo**l
when you ch**ew** your f**oo**d.

a. Always ch____ ____ your food.

b. The bl____ ____ p____ ____l was c____ ____l.

c. Sabrina needs a n____ ____ br____ ____m.

d. I kn____ ____the teacher was in a g____ ____d m____ ____d.

e. The story about the f____ ____lish p____ ____dle is tr____ ____.

8. The **oo** digraph can make different sounds. Sort the words by their sound.

book   wool   boot   zoo   foot   igloo   wood   noon   hoop   cook

oo as in **look**	oo as in **hoot**

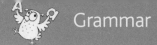
Contractions are words that have been shortened.

> **Sample** was not – wasn't.

The apostrophe takes the place of letters that have been missed out.

9. Write the contractions as full words.

> he is   we are   do not   I am   cannot   it is   let us   is not   I will   there is

a.   don't   _____

b.   I'm   _____

c.   it's   _____

d.   isn't   _____

e.   can't   _____

f.   there's   _____

g.   I'll   _____

h.   he's   _____

i.   we're   _____

j.   let's   _____

10. Write the contraction. Leave out the highlighted letters and add an apostrophe.

a.   sh**e is**   _____

b.   they **a**re   _____

c.   you **ha**ve   _____

d.   we **will**   _____

e.   we **ha**d   _____

f.   you **a**re   _____

g.   he **woul**d   _____

h.   I **ha**ve   _____

i.   did n**o**t   _____

j.   should n**o**t   _____

11. Write shorter sentences by using contractions.

a.   Whatever you do, <u>do not</u> turn around.

_____

b.   <u>There is</u> no lion behind you.

_____

c.   <u>Who is</u> making that roaring sound?

_____

d.   I <u>do not</u> want to look now.

_____

e.   Do you think <u>you will</u> outrun a lion?

_____

Word list

beat	really	legend	thinner	piece	takes	ever	hole
through	newspapers	faster	knees	hero	born	punch	

12. Learn the spellings. Now look and say, picture, cover, write, check.

_____   _____

_____   _____

_____   _____

_____   _____

_____   _____

_____   _____

_____   _____

_____

13. Write any words you got wrong.

_____

14. Write the missing words. Use the word list.

> I only took one **piece** of cake.

  a. Killian wants another _____ of pie.

  b. Manchester United will _____ all other clubs.

  c. A _____ is a story or tale.

  d. Dig a _____ for that plant.

  e. My _____ were shaking with fear.

  f. A boxer could _____ you quite hard.

  g. Have you _____ seen an alien?

  h. Fiona _____ wants a mobile phone for Christmas.

15. In your copybook use these words to make sentences of your own:
through, **thinner**, **takes**, **newspapers**, **faster**, **hero** and **born**.

16. Write the answers. Use the word list.

  a. Write a word with a silent **k**. _____

  b. Find smaller words in these words:

    beat _____ **born** _____ **piece** _____ **through** _____

  c. Write a 3-syllable word. _____

  d. Write a word with a soft **g**. _____

  e. Write a word that ends with a vowel. _____

Drama

17. Work with a group. Recite the poem *The greatest of them all*.
Think about your tone of voice and facial expressions.
Act at being well-known superheroes.

Write about

18. In your copybook write a description of a superhero. It can be from a movie, a comic or one you have made up. Describe the superhero's looks and skills. Write the key words here.

_____

_____

_____

_____

_____

19. Follow the instructions for drawing a superhero. Draw him in your copybook. Give him a name.

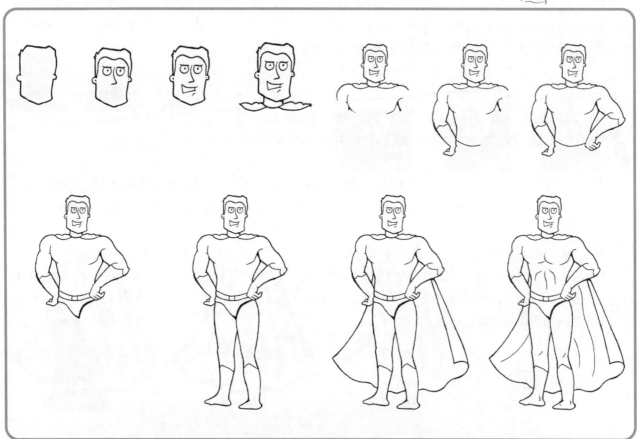

Superman was created in 1932.

Have you ever been on a boat or a ship?
1. Read the text.

The Titanic

In 1912, a luxury ship sailed from
Southampton in England. She was
called the *Titanic* and she was on
her way to New York. It was her first
voyage. The *Titanic* was said to be
the finest and safest ship ever built.

After a brief call in Cobh on 11 April,
the ship headed out into the Atlantic
waters. Then just before midnight on
Sunday the 14 April, a lookout spotted an iceberg. Orders were given for the
ship to turn away, but it was too late. An enormous iceberg scraped along
the side of the ship and made a great hole. Water started to pour in. The
crew were helpless to stop it.

Passengers on board the ship did not know anything had happened but
twenty-five minutes after the accident, an S.O.S. call was put out that the
Titanic was in trouble. Passengers were ordered on deck.

People were lowered into lifeboats in the sea, women and children first. But
there were not enough lifeboats, so some people were left behind. Others
refused to leave their loved ones and stayed on the sinking ship.

The *Titanic* slowly sank. As the end approached, its stern lifted right out of
the water. Then the ship slid forwards and down, the waters closing over her.

A ship answering the S.O.S. call arrived at about 4.00 am and rescued all
those in lifeboats. But it was too late for those that had remained on board.
Of the 2,206 passengers, 1,403 lost their lives. The captain, Edward Smith,
went down with the ship.

The Titanic was built in the
Harland and Wolff shipyard in Belfast.

2. Talk about.

    Talk about the Titanic disaster. How would people
    on board the ship have felt when they knew she
    was going to sink?

3. Answer the questions.

    a. When did the Titanic set sail?

    _____

    b. Where was she sailing to?

    _____

    c. At what time did the lookout spot an iceberg?

    _____

    d. What damage did the iceberg cause?

    _____

    e. Who were the first to be placed into lifeboats?

    _____

    f. How many passengers were on board the Titanic?

    _____

    g. What happened to the captain of the ship?

    _____

4. Write the answers in your copybook.
    a. How many voyages had the Titanic completed?
    b. Why did the ship not turn away from the iceberg?
    c. Why didn't all the passengers get into lifeboats?
    d. Name another situation where you would put out an S.O.S. call.
    e. How many people survived the disaster?

5. In your copybook fill in the facts on a time-line.
    a. The ship filled with water.
    b. A ship arrives at 4.00am.
    c. People get into lifeboats.
    d. The Titanic sank.
    e. An iceberg was spotted.

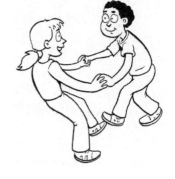

6.   Write the missing letters.

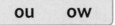

oi   oy

a.   Do not ann___ ___ the teacher.
b.   The children enj___ ___ doing art.
c.   You must j___ ___n hands when you dance.
d.   It is rude to p___ ___nt at people.
e.   The queen is part of the r___ ___al family.

7.   Write your own sentence using **oi** and **oy** words.

_____

8.   Write the missing letters.

ou   ow

a.   The teacher will never sh___ ___t at the class.
b.   Rapunzel was stuck in a t___ ___er.
c.   This lesson is ab___ ___t sounds.
d.   Do you h___ ___l at the moon sometimes?
e.   You are as pretty as a fl___ ___er.

9.   Write your own sentence using **ou** and **ow** words.

_____

10.   Write the missing letters.

au   aw

a.   Stealing is against the l___ ___.
b.   All that pizza will c___ ___se you to feel sick.
c.   The spider might cr___ ___l into your bed.
d.   The month of ___ ___gust comes before September.
e.   My sister is my mother's d___ ___ghter.

11.   Write your own sentence using **au** and **aw** words.

_____

12. Add **ing** to these words.

a. love - _____
b. make - _____
c. trip - _____
d. run - _____
e. sleep - _____

f. cut - _____
g. stop - _____
h. do - _____
i. draw - _____
j. take - _____

13. Write the sentences using opposites for the underlined words.

> One of the words in these sentences need to be changed into **an**.

> interesting   start   right   dangerous   left

a. You have all your sums <u>wrong</u>.

_____

b. Turn <u>right</u> when you get to the big tree.

_____

c. History is a <u>boring</u> subject.

_____

d. It is <u>safe</u> to play in the building site.

_____

e. The teacher wants us to <u>stop</u> working.

_____

14. Write the words in a shortened form.

a. you are _____
b. he will _____
c. have not _____
d. I have _____
e. he would _____
f. were not _____
g. has not _____
h. should have _____
i. would have _____
j. it is _____

The teacher **should've** given us cake.

> **Remember** It is **should have, would have, might have NOT should of, would of, might of.**
> He **should have** eaten his dinner.

Word list

| ship | minutes | given | turn | pour | crew | midnight | lifeboats |
| helpless | voyage | women | others | started | those | forwards | |

15. Use the method: Look and Say, Picture, Cover, Write, Check.

_____   _____
_____   _____
_____   _____
_____   _____
_____   _____
_____   _____
_____

16. Write any words you got wrong.

_____

17. Fill in the missing words. Use the word list.

> At **midnight** your coach will turn into a pumpkin.

a. _____ is the same as 12.00 am.

b. Please _____ me a cup of tea.

c. There are sixty _____ in one hour.

d. Mum has _____ me a long list of chores.

e. _____ children who have finished their work may relax.

f. _____ off the light when you leave the room.

g. I have _____ going to karate lessons.

h. Some may think school is great, _____ won't.

18. In your copybook, use these words to make sentences of your own:
ship, **crew**, **lifeboats**, **women**, **helpless**, **voyage** and **forwards**.

19. Write the answers. Use the word list.

a. Find smaller words in these words from the list:

given _____ **pour** _____ **others** _____ **women** _____

b. Break **midnight** and **lifeboats** into two words.

c. Write the root of these words:

minutes _____ **given** _____ **helpless** _____

d. How many words from the list have 1 syllable? _____

e. How many words from the list have 2 syllables? _____

Drama

20. Work with a group. Give a news report on the *Titanic* disaster. Roles should include a newsreader, reporters from near the scene, and survivors being interviewed.

Write about

21. Imagine you were a *Titanic* survivor. Write your diary entry for the day. Write a rough draft here. Rewrite it neatly in your copybook. Make it look old by rubbing a cool, damp teabag on it.

> The wreck of the Titanic was discovered on 1st September 1985.

22. Fit the words into the grid.

						T					
	s										
	i										

ship	S.O.S.	iceberg	lifeboat	sink
voyage	deck	England	April	Titanic

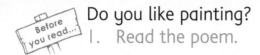

Do you like painting?
1. Read the poem.

The painting lesson

'What's THAT, dear?'
asked the teacher.

'It's Mummy,' I replied.

'But mums aren't green and orange!
You really haven't TRIED.
You don't just paint in SPLODGES
You're old enough to know
You need to THINK before you work....
Now – have another go.'

She helped me draw two arms and legs,
A face with sickly smile,
A rounded body, dark brown hair,
A hat – and, in a while,
She stood back (with her face bright pink):
'That's SO much better – don't you think?'

But she turned white
At ten to three
When an orange-green blob
Collected me.

'Hi, Mum!'

Trevor Harvey

> The famous painter Van Gogh
> cut off part of his left ear.

2. Talk about.
    What do you think the teacher might
    have said when she saw the child's Mum?

3. Answer the questions.
    a.   What picture was the child painting?

    _____

    b.   What colours did he or she use?

    _____

    c.   Name one thing the teacher said.

    _____

    d.   What did the teacher do?

    _____

    e.   What was in the new picture?

    _____

    f.   Was the teacher pleased with this picture?

    _____

    g.   At what time was the child collected?

    _____

4. Complete the sentences and write them in your copybook.
    a.   The title of the poem is
    b.   The poet's name is
    c.   The teacher said the child had not
    d.   The teacher said the child should
    e.   The teacher turned white because

5. Draw the first and second pictures the child might have drawn.

Get your clues from the poem.

6. Write the missing letters.

    | oo   ew   ue |

    a.   The child dr___ ___ a picture of a shr___ ___.
    b.   You must stand in a que___ ___ for your f___ ___d.
    c.   The bird fl___ ___ in the bl___ ___ sky.
    d.   My page is l___ ___ se so I will gl___ ___ it.
    e.   The space cr___ ___ went to the m___ ___n.

7. The **oo** sound can make different sounds. Sort the words by their sound.

    | mood   shook   soot   soon   too   stood   loop   hook   troop   woof |

oo as in **look**	**oo** as in **hoot**

8. Make words. Circle the nonsense words.

I drew a shrew!

    Add **aw**.   Add **ow**.   Add **ew**.
    cr___ ___   cr___ ___   cr___ ___
    dr___ ___   dr___ ___   dr___ ___
    n___ ___   n___ ___   n___ ___
    s___ ___   s___ ___   s___ ___
    fl___ ___   fl___ ___   fl___ ___
    l___ ___   l___ ___   l___ ___
    r___ ___   r___ ___   r___ ___

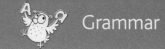
9. Choose the correct verbs to complete the sentences. Rewrite the sentences in your copy book.

> ride   listens   jumps   work   talks   write   eat   sing

a. My brother _____ on the trampoline.
b. I like to _____ beans on toast.
c. I _____ my bike every day after school.
d. You should _____ hard at school.
e. I must _____ a letter to my friend in England.
f. Mum _____ to classical music.
g. I like to _____ loudly during choir practise.
h. My sister _____ to her friend on the telephone.

10. Write the words in alphabetical order.
a. star, silly, sand, sweet, spin

  _____

b. brain, butter, bend, black, book

  _____

c. thank, tower, ticket, train, take

  _____

d. phone, post, prank, push, plane

  _____

e. fudge, friend, flop, find, fetch

  _____

11. Correct the sentences. Use a red pen if you can.
a. leanne went to america in the hallowe'en holidays
b. nick and i went to visit mr. snooty on saturday
c. where did you put emily's lunchbox
d. this december the class is going to a play in dublin
e. why is miss doony shouting at paul
f. may i borrow your book on france
g. jack and jill went up a hill in mayo
h. i went to see dr. green on thursday because i had a sore thumb

Word list

aren't teacher orange haven't tried paint you're enough
replied smile stood lesson bright better collected

12. Use the method: Look and Say, Picture, Cover, Write, Check.

_____   _____

_____   _____

_____   _____

_____   _____

_____   _____

_____   _____

_____

13. Write any words you got wrong.

_____

14. Fill in the missing words. Use the word list.

a.   Have you even _____ to do these sums?

b.   _____ is a bright colour.

c.   I don't have _____ money to buy a game.

d.   Diane felt _____ after having a sleep.

e.   When we asked the teacher for a break,

she _____ that we couldn't.

f.   Why did you _____ your room purple?

g.   This _____ is about learning words.

h.   The boy _____ in the rain until his Mum came.

That's **enough** peas Mum.

15. In your copybook use these words to make sentences of your own:

aren't, **teacher**, **haven't**, **you're**, **smile**, **bright** and **collected**.

16. Write the answers. Use the word list.

a.   Find smaller words in these words from the list:

lesson _____   **orange** _____

teacher _____   **bright** _____

b.   Write the shortened words in full:

haven't _____   **aren't** _____

you're _____

Drama

17. Work with a friend. Recite and act out the poem *The painting lesson*. Think about your tone of voice and facial expressions.

Write about

18. In your copybook write the story of the poem in your own words. Draw a picture to go with it. Write your ideas here.

19. Write the artists on the word ladder. Use the surnames only. The next artist must begin with the last letter of the previous one.

Leonardo da Vinci
Anthony van Dyck
Peter Paul Rubens
Alexander Ivanov
Jan Steen
J.M.W. Turner
Ronnie Landfield
Paul Nash
Derek Hill

Claude Monet

Campbell's Soup Cans is a famous painting by Andy Warhol.

Gill Education
Hume Ave
Park West
Dublin 12

www.gilleducation.ie

Gill Education is an imprint of M.H. Gill & Co

Copyright © Janna Tiearney 2007
Commissioning Editor: Helen Dowling
Managing Editor: Maggie Greaney
Publishing Consultant: Gay Judge
Designer: Derry Dillon
Print Origination: Design Image
Illustrator: Derry Dillon

First published April 2007

ISBN: 978-1-84450-091-8

Acknowledgements:
The Greatest of Them All by Clive Webster used by permission of Macmillan Children's Books, London, UK.

Every effort has been made to trace copyright holders but we could be glad to rectify any omissions at the next reprint.